ELECTRONICS FOR THE SERVICE ENGINEER

PART 2, BOOK 1

ELECTRONICS FOR THE SERVICE ENGINEER

PART 2, BOOK 1

A Textbook for the City and Guilds of London Institute Course No. 224

(as revised 1984 — 1986)

and for

The Technician Education Council Level II Course in Electronics

by
IAN R. SINCLAIR
B.Sc., M.I.E.E.
Formerly Lecturer in Physics & Electronics,
Braintree (Essex) College of Further Education

Revised by

GEOFFREY E. LEWIS

B.A., M.Sc.

Formerly Senior Lecturer in Radio, Television and Electronics,
Canterbury College of Technology

TECHNICAL PRESS
an imprint of
Gower Publishing Company Limited

Published by
Gower Publishing Company Limited,
Gower House,
Croft Road,
Aldershot,
Hants GU11 3HR,
England

Gower Publishing Company,
Old Post Road,
Brookfield,
Vermont 05036,
U.S.A.

British Library Cataloguing in Publication Data

Sinclair, Ian R.
  Electronics for the service engineer: a textbook for the City and Guilds of London Institute course no. 224
  (as revised 1984–1986) and for the Technician Education Council Level II course in electronics. — 2nd ed.

  Pt. 2   Bk. 1
  1. Electronic apparatus and appliances — Maintenance and repair
  I. Title   II. Lewis, Geoffrey E.
  621.381′028′8   TK7870.2
  ISBN 0-566-02575-2

Typeset by Graphic Studios (Southern) Ltd, Godalming, Surrey.
Printed in Great Britain at The Pitman Press, Bath

TABLE OF CONTENTS

Chapter

SECTION 1
Basic Principles and Circuitry

CHAPTER 1

Measurements and Readings

Since the servicing of all electronic circuits calls for the use of measuring instruments, it is necessary to be able to make effective use of the readings obtained.

The two most important types of circuit measurements are **d.c. voltage readings,** using the multimeter, and **signal waveform measurements,** using the cathode-ray oscilloscope.

One preliminary point of importance is that, whatever the type of measurement made in an electrical or electronic circuit, the very act of connecting the measuring instrument into the circuit is likely to have some effect on the circuit, and so to affect the reading obtained.

Multimeters

Multimeters, as their name suggests, are instruments capable of measuring several ranges, usually of d.c. voltage and current, of resistance and of a.c. voltage. Only a few multimeters made nowadays include a.c. current scales, since readings of a.c. current can only be made if a current transformer is included in the meter.

Both analogue and digital meters are now in general use. An analogue multimeter uses a dial and a pointer needle. The required reading is the figure on the dial directly under the tip of the pointer. Analogue multimeters use a moving-coil movement which itself takes some current from the circuit under test, to operate the meter movement.

(a) **Analogue Type.**   (b) **Digital Type.**

Fig. 1.1 **METERS.**

Digital multimeters, on the other hand, contain no moving parts; the reading appears as a figure displayed on a readout similar to that of a calculator. A separate power supply, usually a battery, is used, so that practically no current is drawn from the circuit being tested.

Exercise 1.1
Connect the circuit shown in Fig. 1.2 and use an analogue multimeter to measure the voltage V. Note the results. Check by calculation that V should be 4.5V when the meter is not connected.

If a digital multimeter is also available, use it to measure the voltage V for each circuit.

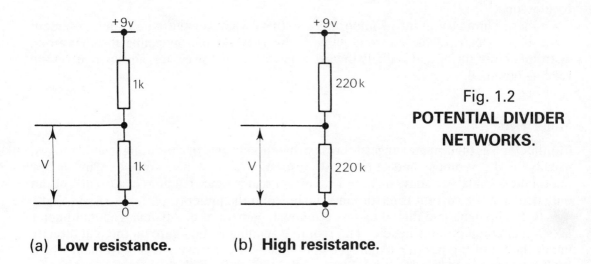

Fig. 1.2
POTENTIAL DIVIDER NETWORKS.

(a) **Low resistance.**   (b) **High resistance.**

The Effect of Meters on Circuits

As the results obtained in *Exercise 1.1* show, the lower resistance of the analogue meter can cause the readings it takes to be unreliable. These unreliable voltage readings are especially apt to be obtained when the resistance of the meter itself is not high compared with the resistance across which the meter is connected.

Fig. 1.3 shows a bias circuit for a transistor. If the voltage at the base of the transistor be measured by connecting a multimeter between the base and supply negative, some current will be found to flow through the resistance of the multimeter; for this resistance is connected in parallel with the resistor R_2 in the circuit itself.

For reliable readings, the resistance of the multimeter must be high compared with R_2. At least ten times higher is the minimum — yet even with a meter resistance ten times the resistance it is connected across, some difference between the true voltage (when no meter is present) and the measured voltage must be expected.

Example: A transistor bias circuit having a 9V supply consists of a 68k and a 15k resistor arranged as in Fig. 1.3.

(*a*) What is the bias voltage on the base (assuming negligible base current)?
(*b*) What voltage will be measured by a voltmeter whose resistance is 150k?

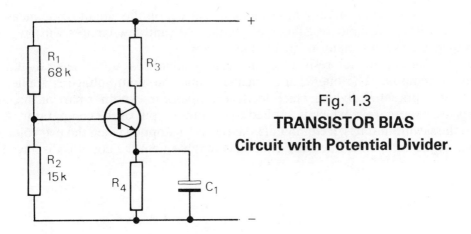

Fig. 1.3

TRANSISTOR BIAS

Circuit with Potential Divider.

Solution: The circuit is a potential divider.

(*a*) For such a circuit, $V = \dfrac{ER_2}{R_1 + R_2}$, with E = 9V, R_1 = 68k and R_2 = 15k.

$$\therefore V = \frac{9 \times 15}{68 + 15} = 1.63V,$$ which is the base bias voltage.

(*b*) The meter will be connected in parallel with the 15k resistor, so that the combined resistance will be $\dfrac{15 \times 150}{15 + 150}$= 13.6k. This quantity must now replace R_2 in the formula above, and the reading becomes:—

$$V = \frac{ER_2}{R_1 + R_2}$$ with E = 9V, R_1 = 68k and R_2 = 13.6k

$$\therefore V = \frac{9 \times 13.6}{68 + 13.6} = 1.5V.$$

The difference is 0.13V, which is about 8% low.

When the analogue meter is used for voltage readings, therefore, it is essential that the resistance of the meter for each voltage range be known.

The meter resistance can be found from the "ohm-per-volt" figure, or "figure-of-merit", which is printed either on the meter itself or in the instruction booklet covering its use. To find the resistance of the meter on a given voltage range, multiply the figure-of-merit by the voltage of the required range.

Example: What is the resistance of a 20kV voltmeter on its 10V range?

Solution: Meter resistance is 20k × 10 = 200k on the 10V range.

If the reading to be taken is across a high resistance, a high-resistance meter range must be used. Sometimes, it is even possible to use to advantage a higher meter range than the one which seems to be called for. For example, if a voltage of around 9V is to be measured and the 10V range of the meter has too low a resistance, the 50V or even the 100V range can be used to reduce the distorting effect of the meter on the circuit.

Note, however, that this would not be possible if the reading on the 100V range would thereby be made too low. A voltage of around 1.5V or less would be unreadable on the higher-range scales.

Digital multimeters generally have much less effect on the circuit being measured. Most of them have an input resistance of about 10M, and few circuits will be greatly affected by having such a meter connected into them.

Meters with still higher resistances are also available — up to several thousand megohms, if required. The operating principle is that the input voltage is applied to a high-resistance potential divider which feeds a *comparator*. Another part of the circuit generates a sawtooth wave which is applied to the other input of the comparator. At the time that the sawtooth starts, a counter also starts and is stopped when the two voltages at the inputs of the comparator become equal. At that moment the count is displayed.

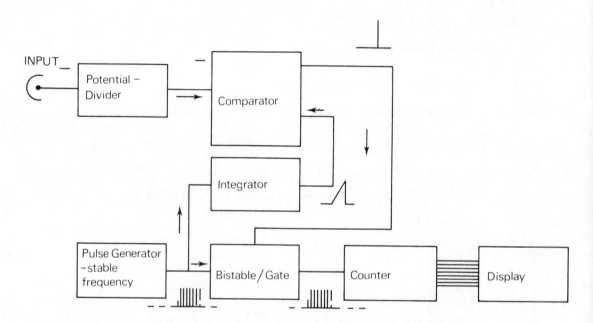

Fig. 1.4 **Block Diagram of a DIGITAL METER.**
(Omitting details of Hold-and-Measure cycle arrangements).

The circuit is arranged so that each digit of the count corresponds to a unit of voltage, say one millivolt, so that the display reading is of voltage. The range switch selects the part of the potential divider to be used, and the position of the decimal point on the display.

Current Readings

In most circuits, the use of a multimeter for current readings has much less effect on the circuit than has its use for voltage readings, provided only that no signal currents are present. To make a current reading, however, the circuit has to be broken, and this is seldom easy on modern circuit boards.

A few audio and TV circuits make provision for checking currents by having a low resistance connected to the current path. By measuring the voltage across this resistor, the current can be calculated using Ohm's Law:

$$I = V/R$$

Because the resistance so placed in the circuit is very small, the effect of connecting the meter into the circuit is negligible.

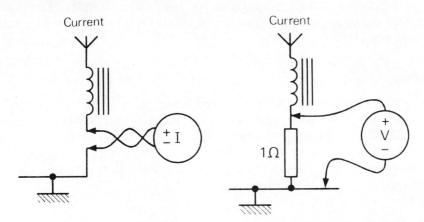

(a) **Breaking the Circuit.**   (b) **Use of a Monitoring Resistor with the Voltmeter.**

Fig. 1.5 **CURRENT MEASUREMENT TECHNIQUES.**

Using the Multimeter in Circuits

The rules to be followed are these:—

1. Start with the meter switched to its highest voltage range.
2. Connect the meter with the circuit switched off.
3. For voltage measurements, always use the highest range that gives a readable output.
4. For current measurements, always try the high-output range first.
5. Never leave the meter switched to any current range when you have temporarily stopped using it.
6. Make sure you know which scale on the dial to read before you try to take a reading.

The increasing popularity of digital multimeters is due to the clear readings of voltage which can be obtained by using them, combined with their high accuracy and the fact that they produce no reading problems and little or no disturbance of the circuit. Some of the more expensive of them are also self-ranging, meaning that no range switch is needed, simply a selector of voltage, current or resistance. The position of the decimal point is then controlled by the circuits inside the meter.

The a.c. voltage ranges of a multimeter are less often used, and should be reserved for checking mains voltage and the a.c. outputs from power supply transformers. These voltage ranges are scaled so that the meter reads r.m.s. voltage for a sine-wave input but will not (except for a few true-r.m.s. digital meters) read the r.m.s. value of any other waveform.

Because a moving-coil meter cannot read a.c. voltage (the average value of voltage over an a.c. cycle is always zero, which is what the meter would have to record), a *rectifier bridge* has to be used inside the meter for a.c. ranges. This rectifier, however, is inefficient both at low voltages and at high frequencies (certainly over 20kHz). The a.c. voltage ranges of the multimeter should therefore not be used as a substitute for the oscilloscope when measuring waveforms.

Voltage Readings

Voltage readings are used to check the d.c. conditions in a circuit. These readings are therefore generally made when no signal is present. Readings taken when a pulse signal is present will obviously give misleading results because of the effect of the pulse signal itself on the meter. For this reason, voltage readings shown on a circuit diagram are usually specified as "no-signal" voltage levels, or are shown only at points in the circuit where the signal is decoupled so that only d.c. is present.

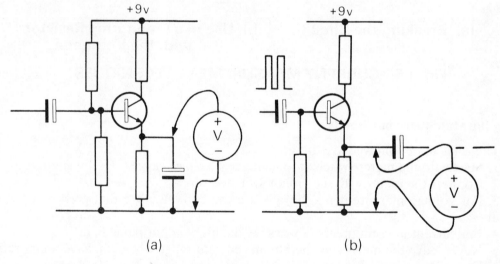

(a)   (b)

Fig. 1.6

In the linear amplifier circuit shown in Fig. 1.6(a), the voltage reading at the emitter will not change greatly even if a small signal is present. In Fig. 1.6(b), however, emitter voltage will be zero when no signal is present, so that the presence of any signal will cause a voltage of some sort to be recorded.

When voltage readings are shown, they are always *average* readings, which may vary from one circuit to another of the same type because of component tolerances. Moreover, the actual readings taken in a circuit may be different from these values, either because of tolerances or because of the use of a meter with a different figure-of-merit, even if the circuit is working quite normally. Some experience is needed to decide if a voltage reading which is higher or lower than the stated average value represents a fault, or whether it is simply due to tolerances or meter resistance.

In general, a voltage varying from the norm by up to 10% can safely be attributed to tolerances; but a voltage variation that shows a transistor to be nearly bottomed or cut-off in a linear stage always betrays a fault condition.

The CRO

The *cathode ray oscilloscope* (CRO) needs to be used in place of a meter of any kind in circuits (especially TV and industrial ones) in which voltage amplitudes, wave-shapes and accurate pulse timing are more important than d.c. bias levels. In many such circuits, transistors are cut off or bottomed when no signal is present, so that bias readings are of little interest in any case, save possibly as a check.

Like the multimeter, the CRO will disturb the circuit into which it is connected for waveform voltage readings. Its input resistance is usually around 1M, unless a high-resistance probe is fitted. The trace is measured against the centimetre (cm) scale on the graticule — the lined transparent sheet (often coloured green) located over the screen of the tube face.

To measure the peak-to-peak amplitude of a signal, the vertical distance, in cm, between one peak and the opposite peak must be taken, using the graticule divisions. This distance, *(Y in Fig. 1.7),* is then multiplied by the figure of sensitivity set on the *VOLTS/CM* input sensitivity control.

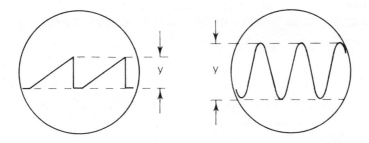

Fig. 1.7   **Measuring AMPLITUDE PEAK-TO-PEAK.**

To measure the duration of a cycle of a.c. from one peak to the next similar peak, the horizontal distance between similar peaks is taken, using the graticule scale and then multiplying this distance, in cm, by the figure of time calibration on the *TIME/CM* switch. From the reading of wave duration for a complete cycle, the frequency of the wave can be found from the formula:—

$$\text{Frequency} = \frac{1}{\text{Time of one Cycle}}$$

With time measured in units of seconds, the calculated frequency will be given by the formula in hertz (Hz). If the time be measured in milliseconds (ms), the frequency will be in kilohertz (kHz); if in microseconds (μs), the frequency will be in Megahertz (MHz).

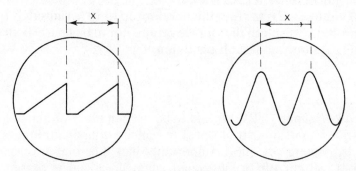

Fig. 1.8   **Measuring the DURATION of a cycle of A.C.**

In some oscilloscopes, a continuously variable *TIME/CM* control needs to be turned to one end of its travel when time measurements are made, and any *X-GAIN* control has to be at its minimum setting.

Using Trigger Inputs

An oscilloscope fitted with an *external trigger (EXT.TRIG)* input can be used for comparing the phases of two waves if a double-beam CRO is not available. A wave into the *EXT.TRIG* input, with the trigger selector switch set to *EXT.*, will cause the timebase to be triggered by that wave, so that the timebase always starts at the same point in the wave.

The triggering wave can be seen on the screen by connecting the *Y-INPUT* socket to

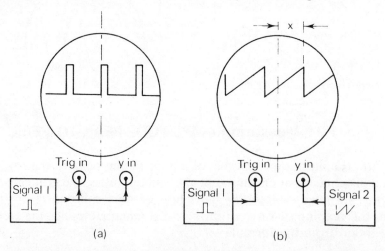

Fig. 1.9   **Using an EXTERNAL TRIGGER to measure a Time Difference.**

the same source. The X and Y shifts can be used to locate one peak of the wave over the centre of the graticule (Fig. 1.9(a)).

If the Y-$INPUT$ be now disconnected from the first wave and connected instead to a second source at the same frequency, a locked trace will appear on the screen (Fig. 1.9 (b)). If there is a time difference between the waves, the peak of the second wave will not be over the centre of the screen, for the timebase is still being triggered by the first wave. Measuring horizontally the distance X from the centre permits calculation of the time shift —either earlier (left of centre) or later (right of centre)—of the second wave as compared with the first.

This time difference can be converted into phase angle if the waves are sine waves. The conversion formula is:—

$$\theta = \frac{360 \times t}{T}$$

where θ is the phase angle in degrees, t the time difference and T the time of a complete cycle expressed in the same units as t.

Example: A complete cycle of a waveform takes 3ms, and a second wave has its peak shifted by 0.5ms. What is the phase difference between the two waves?

Solution:
$$\theta = \frac{360 \times t}{T}$$

$$= \frac{360 \times 0.5}{3}$$

$$= 60°$$

Capacitance and Input Resistance of a CRO

The input resistance of a CRO will disturb the d.c. conditions of a circuit if the circuit resistance is high (100k or so). The input capacitance of a CRO will also affect the signal waveform in the circuit if the circuit resistance is large.

The input capacitance of the CRO is generally around 30pF at the input socket, but will be much greater if a screened cable, or even a "low-loss" coaxial cable, is used as a connector between the CRO and the circuit. An input capacitance of 100pF is quite normal when a fairly short length of such cable is used, and this input capacitance shunts the signal. If the signal comes from an output resistance of more than a few hundred ohms, the effect on the leading and trailing edges of square waves, or on the sine-wave frequency response, can be very noticeable. In effect, the combination of circuit output resistance and CRO input capacitance acts as an integrator or low-pass filter.

When the CRO is used to measure pulses in medium-to-high resistance circuits (a few kilohms or more), a low-capacitance probe should be used. Such probes are available as extras for most types of oscilloscopes. A few probes are active (*i.e.,* they contain transistors or FET's), but most are passive, containing only a variable capacitor and a resistor (Fig. 1.10 (a)). The input voltage is divided down, so that a more sensitive voltage range must be selected; but the effect of capacitance is greatly reduced because the capacitance of the cable and the CRO input is used as part of the divider chain.

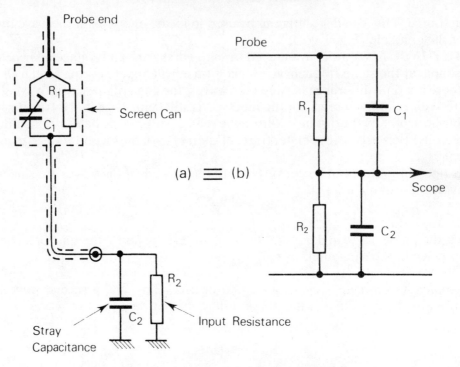

Fig. 1.10 **A Low-Capacitance PROBE.**

In the equivalent circuit of a low-capacitance probe shown in Fig. 1.10 (b), C_2 includes the stray capacitances of the cable and of the oscilloscope. C_1 is varied until $R_1 C_1 = R_2 C_2$. Since signal attenuation is given by the expression:— $\dfrac{R_2}{R_1 + R_2}$, it is clear that a more sensitive oscilloscope range must be chosen.

Tables and Graphs

Tables of values and graphs of variables are two ways of presenting information so that the eye can take in the information easily and quickly.

For comparing sets of voltage readings taken on a circuit, with one set normal and some sets indicating faults, the table is the best method of presentation. The voltage reading points should be arranged in order, and the readings shown clearly. The measuring units also given in Fig. 1.11 show an example of such a Table.

When a series of readings of one quantity is taken with its size varying with every reading, and it is desired to measure the effect that each change has on another quantity, the results can be shown in a table (or *tabulated*); but a *graph* is a much better method of showing the connection.

Say it is desired to measure the base current of a transistor over a range of values from 1μA to 100μA and to take a reading of collector current for each value of base current. The results are first tabulated and then graphed. It will be found that the graph will show at once much more than can be gleaned after much effort from the table.

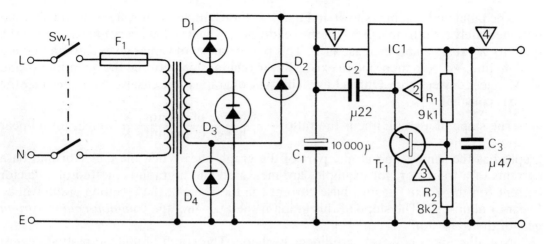

TABLE OF VOLTAGE READINGS

POINT	1	2	3	4
VOLTAGE	39	12	11.4	23

Fig. 1.11

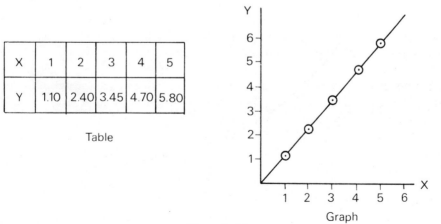

X	1	2	3	4	5
Y	1.10	2.40	3.45	4.70	5.80

Table

Graph

Fig. 1.12

The tabulated readings shown in Fig. 1.12, for example, do not show obviously what is immediately clear from a graph of the readings — which is that every unit change of the quantity X causes a unit increase of Y. This particular set of values gives a graph that is a straight line. There is then said to exist a **linear relationship** between the quantities X and Y. All linear devices obey Ohm's Law. This type of graph is the easiest to use, because the slope is constant.

The slope of a graph line is the ratio:— $\dfrac{\text{Change of quantity Y}}{\text{Change of quantity X}}$ which, for a linear

graph, has the same value at any part of the graph line. When the collector and base currents of a transistor, for example, are measured and a graph is plotted of collector current (on the Y axis) against base current (on the X axis), the resulting graph will be linear or almost so. The slope of this graph is the ratio $\mathbf{h_{fe}}$, the *common-emitter current gain* of the transistor.

Not all graphs, however, are linear in shape. The graph of voltage plotted against time for an a.c. wave, for example, is either a sine wave or a waveform of other shape. A graph of this type is repetitive, and is seldom plotted.

An important graph shape is the **exponential.** This is a graph whose slope values change in such a way that when a given amount is added to one quantity, the other quantity is *multiplied* by another factor. For example, the graph of the collector current, I_c, of a transistor against the base-emitter voltage, V_{be}, is always exponential. For every 60mV increase (or decrease) in V_{be}, the current in the collector is multiplied (or divided) by a factor of 10.

It is typical of an exponential graph that the addition of a constant amount (in this case 60mV) to one quantity (base-emitter voltage) causes the other quantity (current) to be multiplied by another constant factor (ten).

An example of an exponential graph is plotted when a capacitor is charged or discharged through a resistor. It will be recalled that when a capacitor discharges through

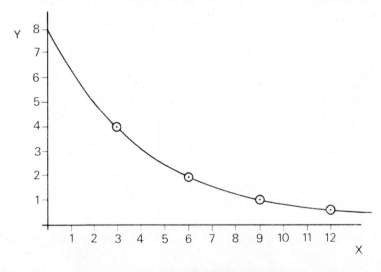

Fig. 1.13   **An EXPONENTIAL Graph.**

a resistor, the time constant RC gives the time for the capacitor voltage to reach 36.8% of its starting value. Because this is an exponential graph, when two time constants have elapsed (a time of 2RC) the voltage will be 36.8% of 36.8% of the starting voltage, or 13.5%. Similarly after the passage of three time constants, the voltage remaining across the capacitor will be only 4.9% of its starting value.

Here again, adding a quantity (the time constant) causes the voltage to be multiplied by another quantity (in this case 36.8%, or 0.368).

Another common shape of graph is the **inverse** graph, pictured in Fig. 1.14. This type of graph is sharply curved in the middle of its range, but almost straight at each extreme, and the nearly-straight portions are almost parallel to the X and Y axes.

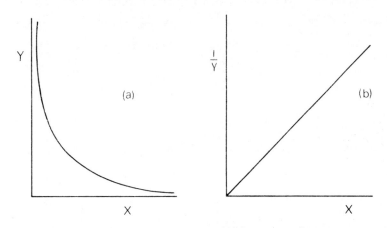

Fig. 1.14 **An INVERSE Graph.**

An inverse graph results when one quantity depends on the *inverse* of the other. Take, for example, a simple d.c. circuit with a fixed voltage, and tabulate values of current I for different values of resistance R. A graph of I plotted against R will give an inverse graph, as shown in Fig. 1.14(a).

If you recognise this as an inverse graph, you can check it by plotting another graph with one of the quantities (but *only* one of them) inverted. For example, plot I against $1/R$, or $1/I$ against R. The result (Fig. 1.14b) would be a straight line.

Waveform Graphs

A waveform graph shows the voltage (or current) that is present in the ciruit *at each instant of time*. Because the quantity being plotted is a voltage (or current), there can be added to it any other voltage (or current) that is present at the same time and at the same place in the circuit. This is called *superposition*.

The simplest example of this occurs when both a steady voltage and a voltage wave are present in the same circuit. The value of steady voltage is added to the wave voltage at every instant, so shifting the whole graph upwards (if the steady voltage is positive) or downwards (if it is negative) by the amount of the steady voltage.

The voltages of other waveforms can also be added. The effect of adding a square wave to a sine wave is shown in Fig. 1.15. Once again, voltages are added *that are present in the circuit at each instant of time*. Waveform addition of this type shows that combinations of sine waves, starting with a fundamental frequency f and adding components at the harmonic frequencies $2f$, $3f$, $4f$, $5f$, etc., yield other familiar wave-shapes such as *square waves* or sawtooth waves, all having the frequency of the fundamental wave.

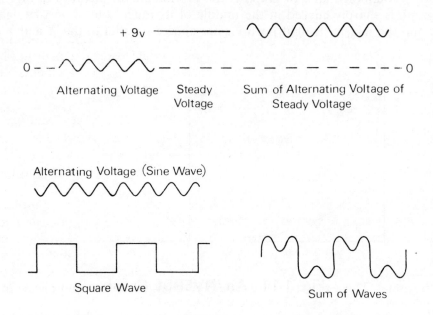

Fig. 1.15 **WAVEFORM ADDITION.**

CHAPTER 2

Semiconductor Diodes

The two most important semiconductor materials, silicon and germanium, have resistivities which lie somewhere between that of a conductor and that of an insulator. The addition of very small amounts of "impurities" such as the elements indium or phosphorus, however, can make both silicon and germanium conduct electric current. The process of adding impurities is called **doping**.

Heating a pure semiconductor above 20°C. also makes the material a better conductor, for as long as it remains at the higher temperature. Good conductors such as copper, and good insulators such as polythene, do not behave like this — neither doping nor heating having so much effect on their conductivity. But the first and most important feature of a semiconductor material intended for use in electronics is that its conductivity can be accurately varied by the addition of small measured quantities of impurities.

Of even greater importance is the fact that not only can the conductivity of semiconductor materials be adjusted to any desired value, but that the *type* of conductivity can be pre-arranged. Most good conductors like copper and silver conduct because they contain a large number of particles called electrons which are free to move between the atoms of the metal. These electrons are negatively charged, so that they always move from the negative pole of the battery towards the positive pole.

Another method of conducting electricity through solids has been known for most of this century — making use of the phenomenon known as "holes". A **hole** behaves in every way like a particle, but can best be described as "the absence of an electron in a place where an electron ought to be". In other words, the hole can be filled by an electron coming from somewhere else — this electron in turn leaving another hole behind it when it moves. Since electrons only move towards the positive pole of a battery, the sequence of holes created when electrons start to move in this way becomes a "reverse flow" of *positive* current moving towards the *negative* pole of the battery.

Note carefully that holes exist only in materials of crystalline structure (like silicon and germanium); and that, unlike electrons, they never leave the crystalline material in which they belong in order to flow through a battery to begin their journey round the circuit again. A hole reaching the negative pole of a battery is extinguished by being filled by an electron. To maintain the flow, a new hole has to be created elsewhere in the crystal itself.

Against this background — which is only a rough sketch of a complex physical process — can now be seen the two different types of impurity which are used to dope silicon or germanium. One type — it includes the elements phosphorus, arsenic and antimony — produces in the semiconductor material an excess of electrons which, when a battery is connected across the material, results in an electron flow (−) to (+) of the normal type. The electrons then become what is known as "the majority carriers" — meaning that most of the current will be carried by them.

The other type of doping impurity — it includes the elements aluminium, gallium and indium — produces an excess of holes, which now become the majority carriers when the battery is connected and current flow begins.

A semiconductor material (say, silicon) in which the majority carriers are electrons is called *N-type silicon*. If indium, on the other hand, be used to dope silicon, the majority carriers will be holes and the doped material is called *P-type silicon*. The letters N and P are used because the electrons are negatively charged and the holes positively charged. Electric current flows in the material when these carriers move.

Junctions

N-type and P-type materials are not particularly important by themselves. But when a single crystal of silicon or germanium has both N-and P-type doping, and the differently-doped parts of the crystal meet, a **junction** is formed.

A junction of this sort is of great importance. A semiconductor junction that forms part of a circuit will (at low voltages) conduct *in one direction only*. The action is illustrated in Fig. 2.1, in which the + and − signs indicate positive and negative carriers respectively.

When the P-type material is connected to the negative pole of a battery, and the N-type material is connected to the positive pole of the same battery, both types of carriers are pulled away from the junction, which is said to be thus given *reverse bias*. With no charged carriers present at the junction, the junction becomes an insulator. The circuit is not complete and no current flows.

If the connections to the battery are reversed, however, and the junction is given *forward bias*, the effect is to pull both types of carrier across the junction so that the junction conducts and current flows in the circuit. This is how one form of semiconductor diode works.

Diodes can be made from any kind of semiconductor material. The most common materials used are germanium, silicon, and two-element materials such as gallium arsenide or indium phosphide.

Diodes may also have very small junctions — in which case they form what are called *point-contact* diodes. The larger junctions, of course, give rise to the name *junction diode*.

Diodes which are used only for their one-way conduction are called *signal diodes* or *rectifier diodes*. They are indicated by the symbol shown in Fig. 2.2(a). Diodes used for voltage regulation, called *Zener diodes*, are indicated by the symbol in Fig. 2.2(b); while diodes used to give a light signal, called *light-emitting diodes* or *LED*'s, use the symbol shown in Fig. 2.2(c).

The arrowhead part of the diode symbol indicates connection to the part of the diode called the *anode*; the flat bar indicates connection to the part called the *cathode*. For normal (forward) conduction of current, the anode needs to be at a voltage more positive than the cathode.

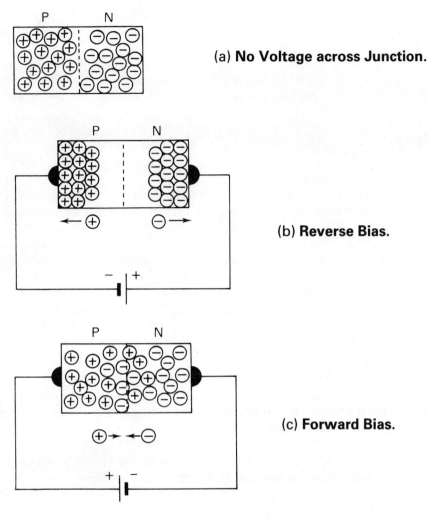

(a) **No Voltage across Junction.**

(b) **Reverse Bias.**

(c) **Forward Bias.**

Fig. 2.1   **A SEMICONDUCTOR JUNCTION.**

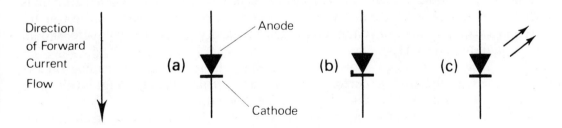

Fig. 2.2   **DIODE SYMBOLS.**
(a) **Signal or Rectifier Diode.** (b) **Zener Diode.** (c) **Light-emitting Diode (LED).**

Exercise 2.1

Use an ohmmeter to identify the anode and the cathode connections of an unmarked diode.

Note that, because of the internal wiring of the ohmmeter, the anode lead of the diode is that which is connected to the *negative* terminal of the ohmmeter when a low resistance is indicated. If a high resistance is indicated, reverse the connections to the diode.

A good diode should indicate a very high resistance when connected one way round, and a low resistance when connected the other way round.

SUMMARY

Semiconductor materials such as silicon and germanium can be made into P-type or N-type conductors by adding small, carefully-measured quantities of impurities to their crystalline structure.

Where P-type and N-type materials meet inside a crystal of semiconductor material, a junction is formed. Such a junction has diode action, in that it conducts in one direction only.

For such a diode to conduct, the connection that must be the more positive is the anode; the more negative connection is the cathode.

Signal and Rectifier Diodes

Signal diodes are used for demodulation, clamping and gating and are often point-contact diodes. These have very small junctions which can pass only small amounts of current; but they have the advantage that the capacitance between anode and cathode is also very small, which is a desirable characteristic of any component used in high-frequency circuits.

Junction diodes having larger-area junctions are better suited to rectifier circuits, which operate at low frequencies but pass large amounts of current.

Exercise 2.2

Connect the circuit illustrated in Fig. 2.3, using a germanium diode.

Turn the potentiometer control so that the voltage across the diode when the circuit is switched on is zero. Make sure that you know the scales of current and voltage you are using — a 1V (or 1.5V) scale of voltage and a 10 mA scale of current. The voltmeter should be of the high-resistance type.

Watching the meter scales, slowly increase the voltage. Note the reading on the voltmeter when the first trace of current flow is detected. This value of voltage is called the *junction potential*. Below this value of voltage the diode does not conduct.

Note the voltage readings for currents of 1 mA, 5 mA and 10 mA. Ask yourself whether the diode obeys Ohm's Law. . .?

Repeat the readings using a silicon diode. What differences do you notice?

Note, lastly, that the voltage across the ammeter (or current meter) can also be measured, but it will be very small compared to the voltage across the diode.

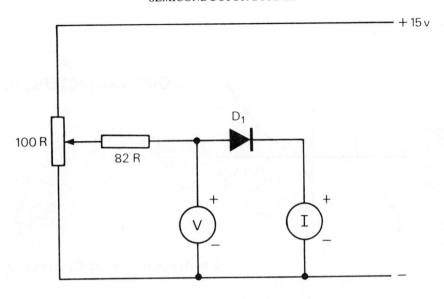

Fig. 2.3

**Circuit for Measuring CURRENT THROUGH DIODE
and VOLTAGE ACROSS DIODE.**

Characteristics of Diodes

A resistor is specified by its values of resistance and power rating, so that asking for a 47k ¼W resistor ensures that the correct item is obtained. Diodes are less easy to specify because they do not obey Ohm's law, and so have no consistently valid resistance value. To specify diodes completely, their **characteristics** have to be given — *i.e.*, graphs of current plotted against voltage in both directions.

Typical characteristics for silicon and for germanium diodes are shown in Fig. 2.4., illustrating the differences between these materials.

The characteristics show *voltage* plotted on the *X-axis*, with forward voltage (anode positive) plotted on the right-hand side and reverse voltage (anode negative) plotted on the left-hand side. Note that the scale used in plotting reverse voltage is very different from the scale used in plotting forward voltage because the voltage values differ so greatly.

Current in the forward direction is plotted on the *Y-axis* above the centre line, with reverse current plotted below the centre line, again on different scales because of the great difference in values. This method of plotting is always used for diode characteristics, so that the scale markings must always be examined very carefully.

The characteristics show clearly the differences between a germanium point-contact and a silicon junction diode:—

1. A higher voltage is needed to make a silicon diode conduct. Typical threshold voltages are 0.5V for silicon, 0.15V for germanium.

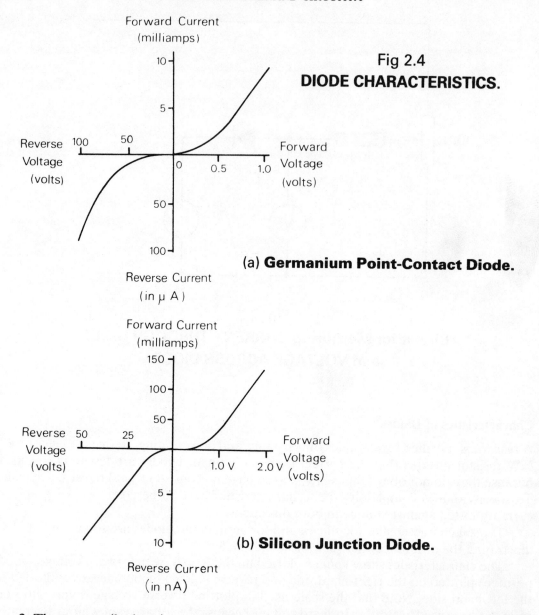

Fig 2.4
DIODE CHARACTERISTICS.

(a) **Germanium Point-Contact Diode.**

(b) **Silicon Junction Diode.**

2. The reverse (leakage) current of a germanium diode is much greater than that of a silicon diode, being measured in μA whereas the silicon is measured in the much smaller nanoampere (1nA = 1/1000μA).

3. A junction diode can pass higher currents than can a point-contact diode.

Zener Diodes and LED's

When a large reverse voltage (larger than the normal voltage across a conducting junction) is applied across a junction diode, the junction will break down so that current flows. This breakdown occurs at a precise voltage whose value depends on the amount of doping in the material and on the way in which the junction is constructed.

It is therefore possible to manufacture diodes which will break down at fixed and predictable voltages. Such diodes are called **Zener diodes**. They are used for voltage stabilisation purposes because the reverse voltage across a conducting zener diode remains almost stable even when the current flow changes considerably.

Exercise 2.3
Connect a Zener diode in the circuit shown in Fig. 2.5, making sure that the cathode of the diode is connected towards the positive pole of the supply. The voltmeter should be set to the 10V range and the milliammeter to the 10 mA range.

Switch on, and adjust the potentiometer so that the voltage across the diode can be read for currents of 1 mA, 5 mA and 10 mA. Note the voltage readings for each of these current values.

If the first reading had been of voltage across an ordinary resistor, what would the voltage reading for 10 mA have been?

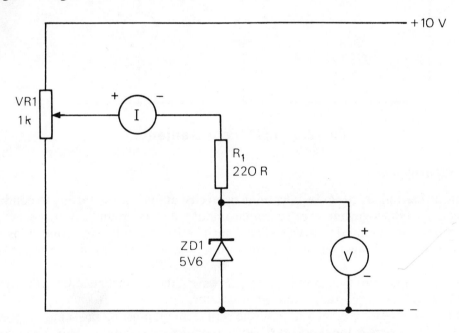

Fig. 2.5 **ZENER DIODE Measurements.**

LED's (*light-emitting diodes*) are diodes made of transparent semiconductor material which makes visible to the user the light generated when current flows through the diode. The semiconductor material used has the property of emitting visible light when current flows through it.

LED's are used as indicators of current flow. They need a higher forward voltage to make them conduct than do either silicon or germanium diodes.

Exercise 2.4

Connect an LED in the circuit shown in Fig. 2.6. The voltmeter should be set to the 5V range and the milliammeter to the 10mA range.

Starting with the potentiometer at its lowest voltage setting, switch on and slowly turn up the voltage until the diode conducts. Note the voltage across the diode which causes current to start flowing.

Examine the light output at current flows of 1 mA, 5 mA and 10 mA, and note the values of forward voltage at these currents.

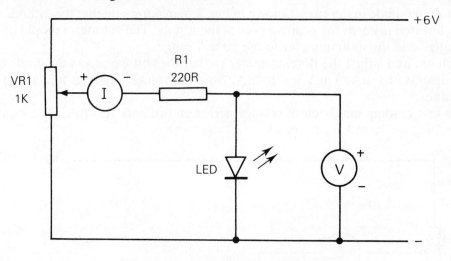

Fig. 2.6   **LED Measurements.**

Selecting Equivalents

When a diode has failed, either by becoming **open circuit (o/c)** or by starting to conduct in both directions (**short-circuit, s/c**), a replacement must be found. If the exact type required cannot be obtained, any equivalent must satisfy the following conditions:

1. The variety of diode (silicon or germanium, point-contact or junction) must be the same.

2. The maximum rated current of the replacement diode must be at least the same as that of the old one, or preferably somewhat greater.

3. The peak reverse voltage rating of the replacement must be the same, or greater.

4. The voltage across the diode at its normal operating current must be the same, or less.

5. Replacements or Zener diodes must have the same voltage and power ratings.

6. Replacements for LED's must have the same colour, forward voltage and current ratings as the ones they replace.

SUMMARY

Diodes can be made of either silicon or germanium, and can be of either the junction or the point-contact type.

Germanium diodes have low forward voltage, but measurable leakage currents. Silicon diodes have higher forward voltages, but almost unmeasurably small leakage currents.

Zener diodes are given reverse-bias, and begin to pass current only at their breakdown voltages, which can be pre-determined.

LED's are diodes giving a visible light output. They need a higher forward voltage than do germanium or silicon diodes.

Rectifier Circuits

The circuit illustrated in Fig. 2.7 is a *half-wave rectifier* circuit — so called because current flows through the diode only for that half of the a.c. wave which is in the forward direction. The output waveform therefore consists of the positive halves of the sine-wave only — with the result that the current output, although it is flowing in only one direction, is not smooth d.c.

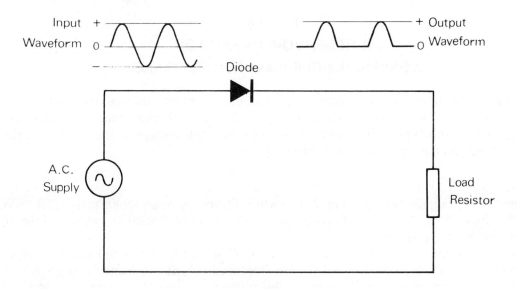

Fig. 2.7
A HALF-WAVE RECTIFIER Circuit.

A d.c. meter connected to the output of the rectifier will record a voltage of less than half the r.m.s. value of the a.c. voltage applied to the rectifier.

The pulses of current through a rectifier circuit are at line (*i.e.*, mains supply) frequency, which is unusable for most electronic equipment. The waveform is greatly improved by inserting a *reservoir capacitor* into the circuit. As its name suggests, this capacitor stores some electric charge while the diode is conducting, then releases the charge to provide current flow when the rectifier is not conducting.

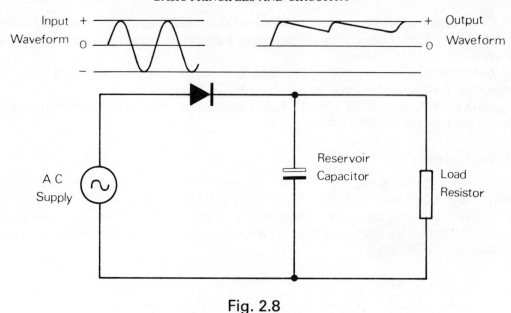

Fig. 2.8
A RESERVOIR CAPACITOR
added to the Half-wave Rectifier Circuit.

If a suitably large value of capacitance be used, current flow through the load resistor can be made continuous rather than coming in half-wave bursts. Moreover, this d.c. voltage will be much greater — almost equal to the peak voltage of the wave — if the capacitor be given a large value and its load current is small.

Exercise 2.5

Connect the circuit illustrated in Fig. 2.9, in which D_1 should be an 1N4001, R_1 470R, ¼W and C_1 470μF, 25V. Set the oscilloscope to the 5V/cm input sensitivity range and the 10 ms/cm timebase speed, and switch on.

First, connect the oscilloscope earth to Point C in the rectifier circuit and its Y-input to Point A. Select *A.C. INPUT* on the oscilloscope. Adjust the controls to produce a visible trace, and switch on the a.c. to the rectifier circuit. If necessary, adjust the oscilloscope sync controls to produce a locked trace. Note the values of peak voltage, and the time interval between positive peaks.

Now disconnect the oscilloscope Y-input from Point A and connect it to Point B instead. Again note peak voltage and wave duration values. Observe the position of the flat "base" of the waveform on the oscilloscope screen, and switch the input to d.c. By how many divisions on the graticule does the trace move upwards when this is done? What d.c. voltage does this indicate?

Connect a multimeter switched to the 10V voltage between B and C ($B+$ and $C-$). The reading shown will be of the average d.c. voltage at this point in the circuit.

Now switch off the rectifier circuit, connect in the reservoir capacitor C_1, and again take the readings between B and C.

Take great care that C_1 is correctly connected, with its positive terminal to the cathode of the rectifier. Capacitors of this type can explode violently if they are wrongly connected into a circuit.

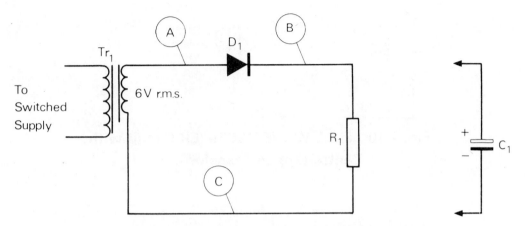

Fig. 2.9   A Measuring Circuit for the Half-wave Rectifier.

The circuit shown in Fig. 2.10 is that of a full-wave rectifier connected to a centre-tapped transformer. Because the centre-tap is earthed, the a.c. voltages at both ends of the secondary winding will be balanced about zero — i.e., when one voltage is at its positive peak, the other will be at its negative peak.

When the winding end marked X is positive, rectifier diode D_1 will conduct. When the winding end marked Y is positive, rectifier diode D_2 will conduct. In this way, both halves of the a.c. wave in turn are connected to the load.

The output voltage, measured with a d.c. meter, will be seen to be twice as high as the voltage output of the half-wave circuit (as would be expected). The frequency of the current pulses is twice supply frequency (100 Hz instead of 50 Hz, 120 Hz instead of 60 Hz).

Note that, for a given amount of load current, a smaller value of reservoir capacitor will be needed to smooth the output into d.c. of a voltage equal to the peak voltage of the wave.

The circuit illustrated in Fig. 2.11 is that of a full-wave bridge rectifier, the most widely used type of rectifier circuit. No centre-tap is needed on the transformer because the arrangement of the diodes is such that the end of the winding which at any one moment is positive is always connected through the diodes to the same end of the load resistor.

Fig. 2.12 shows the path of current through the diodes. In Fig. 2.12(a), current from End X of the transformer winding flows during its positive half-cycle through D_1 and the load, returning to End Y during its negative half-cycle through D_4. When End X is on its negative half-cycle (Fig. 2.12(b)), End Y is positive. Current therefore flows through D_2, the load and D_3, back to End X.

Thus the waveform across the load is that of a complete set of half-cycles in which both halves of the wave are used.

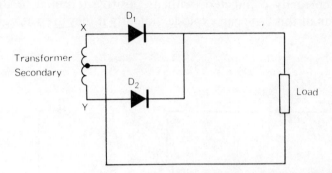

Fig. 2.10   **FULL-WAVE RECTIFIER Circuit with Centre-tapped Transformer.**

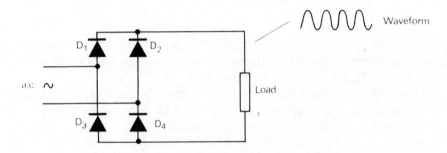

Fig. 2.11   **FULL-WAVE BRIDGE RECTIFIER Circuit.**

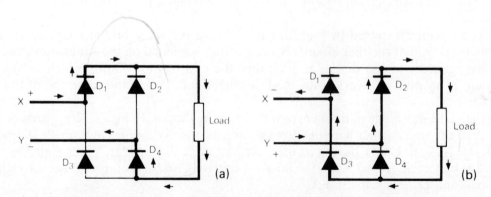

Fig. 2.12   **CURRENT PATHS in the Bridge Rectifier Circuit.**

Exercise 2.6
Connect the bridge rectifier circuit shown in Fig. 2.13, taking care that all the diodes —
they should be 1N4001's or equivalent — are correctly connected. One diode wrongly
connected will become open-circuit as soon as the circuit is switched on, and will at once
cause another of the diodes to become o/c also.

Set the oscilloscope controls to 5V/cm and 10 ms/cm, and switch the circuit on.

Examine the output waveform. Measure the d.c. voltage, using a multimeter on its
25V range connected across the load resistor. Remove any one diode, and study the
effect this has on the waveform.

Now connect into the circuit the reservoir capacitor C_1. Again examine the
waveform across the load, and re-measure the d.c. voltage with the multimeter. Switch
the oscilloscope input to a.c. and to a more sensitive range (say, to 0.5V/cm) so that the
remaining waveform (called the *ripple*) can be seen.

Finally, connect either a 100R, 1W resistor to place of the load resistor or a 220R,
¼W resistor in parallel with the existing one, and observe the change in the ripple
waveform voltage.

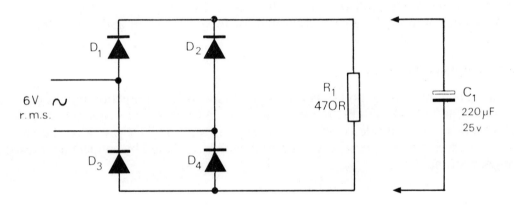

Fig. 2.13

In all rectifier circuits, every diode will be reverse-biased for half of the a.c. cycle.
The amount of this reverse bias depends on the type of circuit used, and is greatest for a
half-wave rectifier feeding into a reservoir capacitor.

The Table on the next page shows the operating results which may be expected
from rectifiers of the three types described — half-wave, full-wave and bridge — given
an a.c. input of E volts peak ($0.7E$ volts r.m.s.) and smoothing by reservoir capacitor.

Note that in all rectifier circuits, reversing the connections of the diodes reverses also
the polarity of the output voltage.

RECTIFIER CIRCUITS — OPERATING CHARACTERISTICS

Circuit	D.c. output (No load)	Reverse voltage on diodes	Ratio I_{dc}/I_{ac}	D.c. output (Full load)
Half-wave	E	$2E$	0.43	$0.32E$
Full-wave	E	E	0.87	$0.64E$
Bridge	E	E	0.61	$0.64E$

The ratio I_{dc}/I_{ac} is the ratio of direct current flow through the load to a.c. input to the rectifier circuit.

SUMMARY

A half-wave rectifier uses a single diode, passing half of the a.c. wave. A full-wave or bridge rectifier passes two positive half-cycles in each cycle.

The addition of a reservoir capacitor brings the output voltage up to almost the peak a.c. value.

The ripple is at supply frequency when a half-wave circuit is used, and at double supply frequency when a full-wave or bridge circuit is used.

All diodes used must be correctly rated for forward current and reverse bias.

The Zener Diode Regulator

A Zener diode, as already noted, is reverse-biased so that the junction breaks down to permit current flow through the diode. This breakdown occurs at a precisely calculated voltage depending on diode construction, and causes no damage provided the current flow is not excessive. To prevent this, current can be regulated by connecting a resistor in series with the diode.

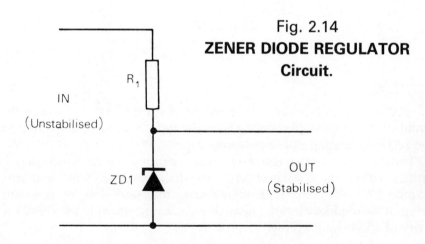

Fig. 2.14
**ZENER DIODE REGULATOR
Circuit.**

R_1

IN
(Unstabilised)

ZD1

OUT
(Stabilised)

The complete circuit is therefore that shown in Fig. 2.14, with the output voltage across the diode being used to supply any other circuit or part of a circuit which requires a stable voltage. Many circuits, especially measuring and oscillator circuits, are adversely affected by voltage variation, which can be caused by changes in the supply voltage or by changes in the current drawn by the load.

Clipping, Clamping and D.C. Restoration Circuits

All these signal-shaping operations (described in Part 1) can be performed with the aid of diodes. A series-connected diode (*i.e.*, one connected as for a half-wave rectifier) will pass only half of a waveform, so that the other half is *clipped* (Fig. 2.15(a)).

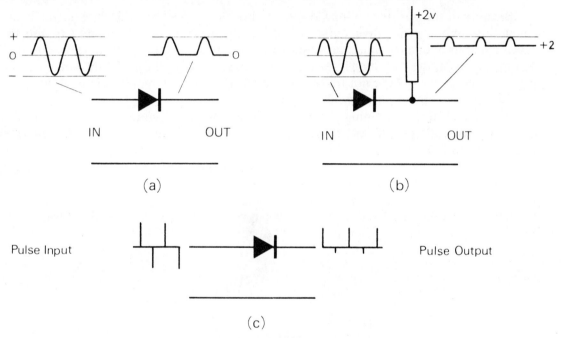

Fig. 2.15 **CLIPPING Circuits.**

If a steady d.c. voltage is applied across the diode in addition to the a.c., a different part of the wave will be clipped. This makes it easy in practice to select any part of a waveform that may be required, and to clip the rest of it. In Fig. 2.15(b), for instance, the addition of a resistor of the appropriate value allows selection of only that part of the waveform whose voltage exceeds 2V; while Fig. 2.15(c) shows how (*e.g.*) the positive pulses only can be selected from a mixed (+) and (−) input.

Note that no capacitor is used in these clipping circuits. If the waveform needs to be fed through a capacitor, a resistor must also be added to prevent the capacitor from retaining charge after the diode ceases to conduct.

The operation of *clamping* restricts the voltage of a waveform to one set value for a short period. A simple diode clamp is shown in Fig. 2.16.

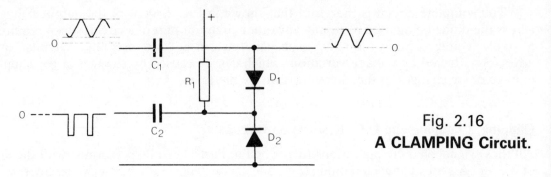

Fig. 2.16
A CLAMPING Circuit.

Because of the positive voltage at their cathodes, diodes D_1 and D_2 are normally not conducting. When a negative pulse is applied to the cathodes, D_1 conducts and the waveform at its anode is momentarily shorted through D_1 and D_2 to earth (ground). The inclusion of D_2 in the circuit ensures that the voltage at the cathodes of the two diodes is just below zero. If D_2 were not there, the clamping voltage would be the negative peak voltage of the clamping pulse, which might vary.

At the end of the clamping pulse, waveform voltage is free to vary again; but now any change of voltage will start from zero, because the capacitor C_1 has been charged through D_1 and D_2.

A *d.c. restoration* circuit is needed when it is necessary to hold some part of a waveform at a specified d.c. level. An example is the TV signal waveform, in which black level is represented by the cut-off voltage of the cathode ray tube. When the signal is either transmitted or passed through a transformer or a capacitor, the d.c. level is lost. An un-restored signal will then have a d.c. level of zero volts.

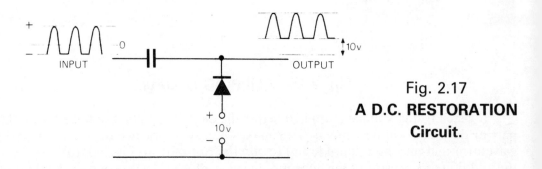

Fig. 2.17
A D.C. RESTORATION Circuit.

A d.c. restoration circuit can set the d.c. level of either peak of a waveform. Fig. 2.17 shows one which restores the most negative part of a waveform to a level of 10V above zero. When any part of the waveform is at less than + 10V, D_1 conducts and charges C_1 to a d.c. voltage of 10V. At one negative peak, C_1 will be charged so that the diode is only just conducting. With the negative peak set to + 10V, the rest of the waveform will also be raised in voltage by the same amount.

Diode Protection Circuits

Fig. 2.18 shows three circuits which use diodes to protect other equipment. Fig. 2.18(a) shows a circuit using germanium diodes connected across the meter movement to protect the meter against overloads. Each diode conducts when the voltage across it reaches about 0.15V, so that no more than this voltage can be applied across the movement in either direction. In most meters, the needle reaches full-scale deflection when the voltage across the coil is 0.1V or less, so that the diodes do not interfere with the normal action of the meter.

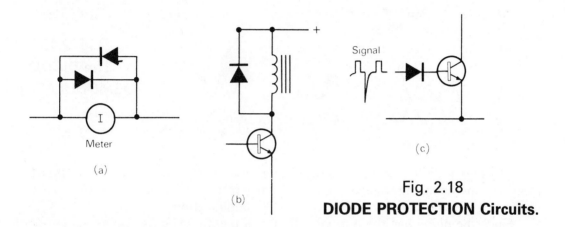

(a)

(b)

Signal

(c)

Fig. 2.18
DIODE PROTECTION Circuits.

Meter

Fig. 2.18(b) shows the circuit of a diode used to protect a transistor which is switching current into an inductive load such as a relay. When the current across such a load is suddenly switched off, the voltage across the load rises to a very high value (many times the supply voltage), which can damage the transistor. A diode connected as shown will conduct when the voltage surge occurs, so protecting the transistor.

Fig. 2.18(c) shows a diode connected so as to protect the base-emitter junction of a transistor from reverse voltage. Many silicon transistors have a base-emitter junction which will break down on the arrival of a quite low negative pulse of voltage (10V or so). The connection into the circuit of a diode having a higher reverse voltage rating than this averts the danger.

Amplitude Demodulation

The circuit of a simple demodulator for amplitude-modulated signals is shown in Fig. 2.19. The action of the diode is similar to that of a half-wave rectifier, passing only half of the modulated radio signal wave. The output of the diode is a signal, still at radio frequency, whose amplitude varies. The average voltage at the output therefore also varies, at the frequency of the modulation.

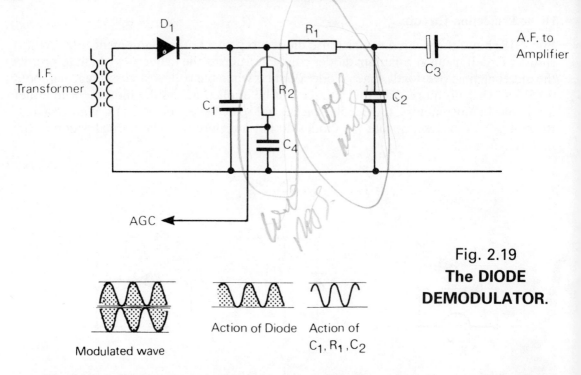

Fig. 2.19

The DIODE

DEMODULATOR.

Modulated wave

Action of Diode   Action of C_1, R_1, C_2

The high radio frequency is shorted to ground by C_1, and the low-pass filter R_1-C_2 removes any remaining trace of radio frequency from the output signal. Capacitor C_3 is used to couple the signal to the next stage of amplification.

Since the diode has the normal action of a rectifier, d.c. is also present — with a voltage equal to the peak voltage of each r.f. wave if it be well smoothed. This d.c. is separated from the audio frequencies at the cathode of the diode by another low-pass filter (R_2C_4), and is then used to provide automatic gain control (AGC).

The capacitor C_3 prevents the d.c. voltage from affecting the bias of the next amplifying stage.

Exercise 2.7

Connect the demodulator circuit shown in the circuit of Fig. 2.20. D_1 should be a germanium diode such as OA90, OA91, IN541, IN490 or IN127. Then connect the oscilloscope with its earth lead to Point D and its Y-input to Point A. Apply to the anode of the diode a signal at 1 MHz, modulated at 400 Hz. Set the Y-input sensitivity of the oscilloscope to 1V/cm and the timebase to 1 ms/cm, and switch on. Adjust for a locked trace and examine the waveform.

Now clip the Y-input of the oscilloscope to Point B, and examine the new waveform which appears. Sketch the waveforms at A and at B, and then connect the Y-input to Point C, sketching this waveform also.

Now use a high-resistance multimeter set to the 2.5V range to measure the d.c. voltage between E and D. Compare the effects on this voltage of (a) varying the amplitude of the 1 MHz signal only, (b) varying the amplitude of the 400 Hz signal only.

If the 400 Hz waveform cannot be varied, switch the modulation on and off alternately, and note the effect on the d.c. level.

The results will show, first, that the demodulated signal is the 400 Hz modulating wave, free of radio frequency; and, second, that the AGC voltage depends on the amplitude of the r.f. carrier, not on the amplitude of modulation, when a normal a.m. signal is applied.

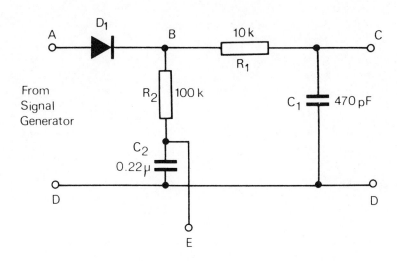

Fig. 2.20

SUMMARY

Diodes are used in voltage regulation (Zener diodes), voltage and current indication (LED's), clipping, gating, clamping and a.m. demodulation. For the last four types of operations, signal diodes with small values of capacitance are preferred.

A diode may fail in either of two ways — *open circuit (o/c)*, when no current can pass in either direction, or *short circuit (s/c)*, when current passes freely in both directions.

Open circuit failures have the following effects:—

(a) The d.c. output of rectifier circuits is either reduced or falls to zero. A half-wave circuit will have no output; full-wave and bridge circuits will have reduced output, with ripple at supply frequency if only one diode fails.

(b) A Zener diode regulator will give a higher voltage output, without regulation.

(c) Clipping, clamping and gating circuits will not work. When the diode is in series with the wave, there will be no output signal. When the diode is in parallel with the wave, the signal will be unaffected by the diode.

(d) There will be no signal from an amplitude demodulator, and no AGC voltage. No detectable r.f. will appear at the cathode of the diode.

Short-circuit failures of diodes have the following effects:—

(a) Rectifier circuits will blow fuses, and electrolytic capacitors may be damaged. A short-circuit diode will usually fuse itself, so becoming open-circuit. In a bridge circuit, a short-circuit diode will usually cause another diode to become open-circuit.

(b) A Zener diode regulator will give zero output.

(c) Clipping, clamping and gating circuits will not work. When the diode is in series with the wave, the output signal will be identical to the input signal. When the diode is in parallel, there will be no output signal at all.

(d) There will be no audio output from an AM demodulator, and no AGC. The still-modulated r.f. wave will then be present at the cathode of the diode.

CHAPTER 3
Transistors and Other Semiconductors

1. BIPOLAR TRANSISTORS

Bipolar transistors each have two junctions and three separate connections, as shown in Fig. 3.1. The NPN transistor (Fig. 3.1.(a)) has a thin layer of P-type material sandwiched between thicker N-type layers; the PNP transistor (Fig. 3.1(b)) has a thin layer of N-type material sandwiched between thicker P-type layers.

The layer which forms the middle of the sandwich is called the **base**; the other two are called the **emitter** and the **collector** respectively.

Figs. 3.1(c) and 3.1(d) illustrate schematically the NPN and the PNP transistor, respectively. In Fig. 3.1(e) the three connections of a transistor are named and indicated. The direction of the arrow-head on the emitter symbol distinguishes the transistor illustrated as being the NPN type. (The arrowhead points in the conventional direction of current flow).

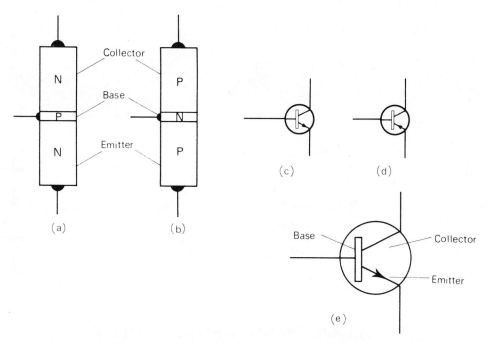

Fig. 3.1 **The BIPOLAR TRANSISTOR.**

35

If the two junctions in any bipolar transistor were far apart ("far" in this case meaning only a few millimetres), current flowing across one junction would have no effect on the other junction. Bipolar transistors are so made, however, that the junctions are very close to one another, so that electrons or holes moving across one junction will nearly all move across the other junction also (Fig. 3.2). The result is that current flowing in one junction controls the amount of current flowing in the other junction. (Bipolar transistors, of course, are so called because both holes and electrons play their parts in the flow of current).

As noted in Chapter 2, a junction is said to be forward-biased when the P-type material is connected to the positive pole of a battery and the N-type material is connected to the negative pole of the same battery of supply.

Imagine now an NPN transistor connected as in Fig. 3.3(a). With no bias voltage, or with reverse bias, between the base and the emitter connections, there are no carriers in the base-emitter junction, the voltage between the collector and the base makes this junction reverse-biased, so that no current can flow in this junction either. The transistor behaves as if it were two diodes connected anode-to-anode (Fig. 3.3(b)). No current could flow in the circuit even if the battery connections were to be reversed.

When the base-emitter junction is forward-biased, however, electrons will move across this junction. Because the collector-base junction is physically so close, most of the

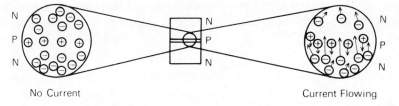

No Current   Current Flowing

Fig. 3.2

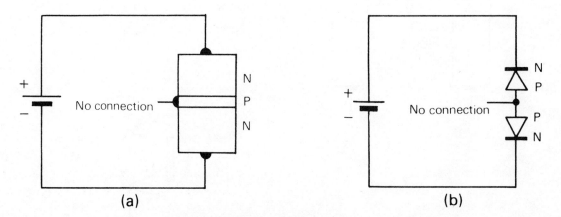

(a)   (b)

Fig. 3.3 **An NPN TRANSISTOR with no Base Bias.**
(a) Schematic. (b) Equivalent circuit.

electrons will move across this junction also, so making it conduct *even though it is reverse-biased.* Any electrons passing across the base-collector junction are then swept towards the positive pole of the supply.

With both junctions conducting, most of the current will flow between the collector and the emitter, since this is the path of lower resistance. The transistor now no longer behaves like two anode-to-anode diodes because the electrons passing through the base-emitter junction make the collector-base junction conduct despite the reverse bias between collector and base.

The current flowing between the collector and the emitter is much greater (typically 25 to 800 times greater) than the current flowing between the base and the emitter.

If the base be now unbiased or reverse-biased again, no current can flow between the collector and the emitter. Thus the current in the base-emitter junction controls the amount of current passing through the collector-base junction.

Exercise 3.1
Using a silicon NPN transistor such as either 2N697, 2N1711, 2N2219 or BFY 50, measure the resistance between leads, using a multimeter set on the ohms scale. Remember that the multimeter polarity (+ and −) markings are reversed when the ohms scale is used, so that the terminal marked (+) is negative for ohms readings and the terminal marked (−) is positive.

Set out your readings as in the table below.

TABLE 3.1

R_{be}		R_{bc}		R_{ce}	
b +	b −	b+	b −	c +	c −

Note that each reading is taken in both directions so that, for example, R_{be} (b+) means a connection between base and emitter with the base (+), and R_{be} (b−) means the same connections but with the polarity reversed.

Note that if the connections to the transistor are unknown, the base lead can be identified since only the base will conduct to the other two electrodes with the same polarity.

When an NPN transistor is tested, the base will conduct to either emitter or collector when the base is positive. The base of the PNP transistor will conduct to both emitter and collector when the base is made negative.

Repeat the tests, and fill in a new table using a PNP transistor such as the 2N2905 or BFX39.

Then try to identify the leads of an unmarked transistor.

Tests with an ohmmeter can identify junction faults. A good transistor should have a very high resistance reading between collector and emitter with either polarity of connection. Measurements between the base and either of the other two electrodes should show one conducting direction and one non-conducting direction. Any variation from this pattern indicates a faulty transistor with either an open circuit junction (no conduction in either direction) or excessive leakage (conduction in both directions).

Current Gain

It has been seen that the amount of current flowing between the collector and the emitter of a bipolar transistor is much greater than the amount of current flowing between the base and the emitter, but that the collector current is controlled by the base current. The ratio:
$$\frac{\text{Collector Current}}{\text{Base Current}}$$ is in fact constant (given a constant collector-to-emitter voltage), and is

commonly called the *current gain* for the transistor (its full name is the *common-emitter current gain*). The symbol used to indicate it is $\mathbf{h}_{fe}$. A low-gain transistor might have a value of h_{fe} of around 20 to 50, a high gain transistor one of 300 to 800 or even more.

Note that the tolerance of values of h_{fe} is very large, so that transistors of the same type — even transistors coming fom the same batch — may have widely different h_{fe} values.

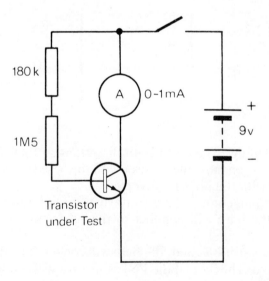

Fig. 3.4

Exercise 3.2

Measure the h_{fe} values for a number of transistors, using a transistor tester.

If a tester is not available, use the circuit of Fig. 3.4 which will give approximate h_{fe} values for a silicon NPN transistor by the current readings on the multimeter when put through the conversion table below:

Meter Reading	h_{fe}	Meter Reading	h_{fe}
1 mA	200	0.5 mA	100
0.9 mA	180	0.4 mA	80
0.8 mA	160	0.3 mA	60
0.7 mA	150	0.2 mA	40
0.6 mA	120	0.1 mA	20

These results are achieved because the two base resistors maintain current flow at about 5µA.

The **characteristics** of a typical silicon transistor are shown in Fig. 3.5. These are the graphs which show the behaviour of the transistor.

Fig. 3.5(a) shows the *input characteristic,* or the I_{be}/V_{be} graph. The slope of the line on this graph gives the input resistance of the transistor, and its steepness shows that the resistance is small. The fact that the graph line is curved shows that input resistance varies according to the amount of current flowing, and is greatest when the current flow is small.

Fig. 3.5(b) shows the I_{ce}/I_{be} characteristic, called the *transfer characteristic.* This graph is a nearly straight line whose slope is equal to the current gain, h_{fe}.

Fig. 3.5(c) shows the *output characteristic,* I_{ce}/V_{ce}, whose slope gives the value of output resistance. The horizontal parts of the graph lines show that a change in collector voltage has almost no effect on collector current flow. It is as if the transistor output had a resistance of very high value in series with it.

These graphs show that a transistor connected with its emitter common to both input and output circuits has a low input resistance, fairly large current gain and high output resistance.

Another characteristic which is very useful is the *mutual characteristic,* I_{ce}/V_{be}, shown in Fig. 3.6 for a typical power transistor. Note the large current values and the nearly straight line of the characteristic.

Although the I_{ce}/V_{be} is often a useful characteristic for an amplifier designer to know, it is not always provided by the transistor manufacturer.

Rules for Substitution

When transistors are substituted one for another, the following rules should be obeyed:—

1. The substitute transistor must be of the same variety (*i.e.,* silicon, NPN, switching as opposed to amplifying, etc.)

2. The substitute transistor should have about the same h_{fe} value.

3. The substitute transistor should have the same ratings of maximum voltage and current.

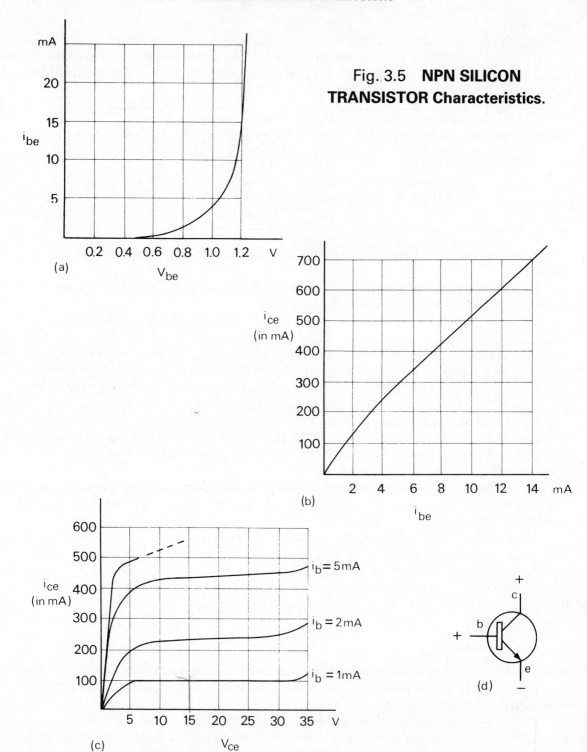

Fig. 3.5 **NPN SILICON TRANSISTOR Characteristics.**

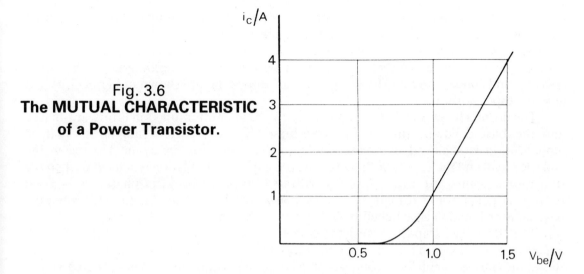

Fig. 3.6
The MUTUAL CHARACTERISTIC of a Power Transistor.

Applications of Bipolar Transistors

Bipolar transistors are used as current amplifiers, voltage amplifiers, oscillators and switches.

An amplifier, as you know, has two input and two output terminals, but a transistor

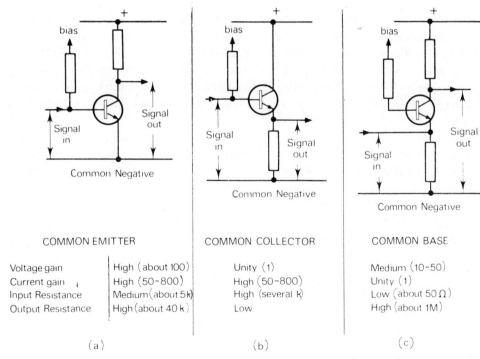

	COMMON EMITTER	COMMON COLLECTOR	COMMON BASE
Voltage gain	High (about 100)	Unity (1)	Medium (10-50)
Current gain	High (50-800)	High (50-800)	Unity (1)
Input Resistance	Medium (about 5k)	High (several k)	Low (about 50 Ω)
Output Resistance	High (about 40 k)	Low	High (about 1M)
	(a)	(b)	(c)

Fig. 3.7 **The Three Circuit Connections of a Bipolar Transistor.**

15   current
       Voltage $\frac{100}{15}$ 6.7Ω

has only three electrodes. It can therefore only operate as an amplifier if one of its three electrodes is made common to both input and output circuits.

Any one of a transistor's three electrodes can be connected to perform in this common role, so there are three possible configurations:— *common-emitter, common-collector* and *common-base*. The three types of connection are shown in Fig. 3.7 (a), (b) and (c) respectively.

The normal function of a transistor when the base-emitter junction is forward-biased and the base-collector junction reverse-biased is as a current amplifier. Voltage amplification is achieved by connecting a load resistor (or impedance) between the collector lead and the supply voltage (see next Chapter). Oscillation is achieved when the transistor is connected as an amplifier with its output fed back, in phase, to its input (Chapter 6). The transistor can also be used as a switch or relay (Chapter 13) when the base-emitter junction is switched between reverse bias and forward bias.

The three basic bipolar transistor circuit connections are shown in Fig. 3.7, with applictions and values of typical input and output resistances given below each. Fig. 3.7(a) shows the normal amplifying connection used in most transistor circuits. The common-collector connection in Fig. 3.7(b), with signal into the base and out from the emitter, is used for matching impedances, since it has a high input impedance and a low output impedance. The common-base connection, with signal into the emitter and out from the collector, shown in Fig. 3.7(c) is nowadays used mainly for VHF amplification.

Transistor Failure

When transistors fail, the fault is either a **short-circuit (s/c)** or an **open-circuit (o/c)** junction; or the failure may possibly be in both junctions at the same time.

An o/c base-emitter junction makes the transistor "dead", with no current flowing in either the base or the collector circuits. When a base-emitter junction goes o/c, the voltage between the base and emitter may rise higher than the normal 0.6V (silicon) or 0.2V (germanium) — though higher voltage readings are common on fully operational power transistors when large currents are flowing.

A s/c base-emitter junction will allow current to flow easily between these terminals with no voltage drop, but with no current flowing in the collector circuit.

The two above faults are by far the most common, but sometimes a base-collector junction goes s/c, causing current to flow uncontrollably.

All of these faults can be found by voltage readings in a circuit, or by use of the ohmmeter or transistor tester when the transistor is removed from the circuit. (A few types of transistor tester can even be used with the transistor still connected into circuit).

SUMMARY

Bipolar transistors consist of three regions — emitter, base and collector — with two junctions. Current flows between collector and emitter only when current flows between base and emitter, and when there is current gain (h_{fe}) at least equal to $\dfrac{I_c}{I_b}$.

The characteristics of a transistor with common-emitter connection show low input resistance, medium output resistance, and values of current gain between 20 and 800 depending on construction.

2. FIELD-EFFECT TRANSISTORS

To be strictly accurate, the so-called "field-effect transistor" is not really a transistor at all. The word "transistor" is a compression of the term "transfer resistor", and the FET (as it is commonly abbreviated) does not work like that at all. It is, in fact, more correctly described as a *field-effect device,* because its operation depends on the presence and effects of an electric field. Nevertheless, the term "field-effect transistor" has become common parlance, so must be used here.

There are two types of field-effect transistor – the *junction FET* and the *Metal-Oxide-Silicon FET, or MOSFET.* Both work by controlling the flow of current carriers in a narrow channel of silicon. The main difference between them lies in the method by which the flow is controlled.

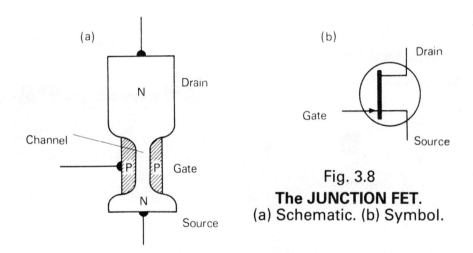

Fig. 3.8
The JUNCTION FET.
(a) Schematic. (b) Symbol.

Look first at the structure of the junction FET (Fig. 3.8). A tiny bar of silicon of either type (the N-type is actually illustrated) has a junction formed near one end. Connections are made to each end of the bar, and also to the P-type material at the junction. The P-type connection is called the *gate,* the end of the bar nearest the gate the *source,* and the other end of the bar the *drain*.

A junction FET of the type illustrated is normally used with the junction reverse-biased, so that few moving carriers are present in the neighbourhood of the junction.

The junction, however, forms part of the silicon bar, so that if there are few carriers present around the junction, the bar itself will be a poor conductor. With less reverse bias on the junction, a few more carriers will enter the junction and the silicon bar will conduct better; and so on as the amount of reverse bias on the junction decreases.

When the voltage is connected between the source and the drain, therefore, the amount of current flowing between them depends on the amount of reverse bias on the gate; and the ratio: $\dfrac{\text{Source-Drain Current}}{\text{Gate Voltage}}$ is called the *mutual conductance,* whose symbol is $\mathbf{g_m}$. This quantity, g_m, is a measure of the effectiveness of the FET as an amplifier of current flow.

For most FET's, g_m values are very low, only about 1.2 to 3 mA/V, as compared with corresponding values for a bipolar transistor of from 40 mA/V (at 1 mA current) to several ampere/volts at high rates of current flow. Because the gate is reverse-biased, however, practically no gate current flows, so that the resistance between gate and source is high — very much higher than the resistance between base and emitter of a working bipolar transistor.

Fig. 3.9 shows the basic construction of the Metal-Oxide-Silicon FET. A *p*-type silicon substrate has two *N*-type regions induced into it, as shown. A very thin *N*-type layer is also induced, to provide a conducting channel between the source and drain regions. Bias voltages are applied to both gate and substrate to control the flow of current between source and drain.

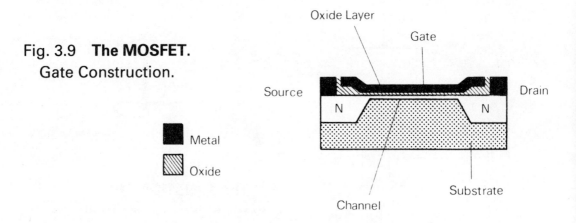

Fig. 3.9 **The MOSFET.**
Gate Construction.

A positive voltage applied to the gate has the effect of attracting more electrons into the channel, and so increasing its conductivity. A negative potential so applied would repel electrons from the channel and so *reduce* its conductivity.

Both *N*-type and *P*-type channel devices can be made. When the voltage applied to the gate has the effect of cutting down the current flow in the channel, operation is said to be *in the depletion mode.* When the gate is used to increase current flow, operation is said to be *in the enhancement mode.*

In most cases, enhancement-mode devices are made without the conducting channel. With the gate-to-substrate voltage equal to zero, the device is then cut off. When a gate voltage which is positive with respect to the substrate is applied, an electric field is set up that attracts electrons towards the oxide layer. These now form an induced channel to support a current flow. An increase in this positive gate voltage will cause the drain-to-source current flow to rise.

Most MOSFET circuits used in practice employ *N*-channel devices in the enhancement mode.

Junction FET's cause few handling problems provided that the maximum rated voltages and currents are not exceeded. MOSFET's, on the other hand, need to be handled with great care because the gate must be completely insulated from the other two electrodes by the thin film of silicon oxide. This insulation will break down at a voltage of 20 to 100 V, depending on the thickness of the oxide film. When it does break down, the transistor is destroyed.

Any insulating material which has rubbed against another material can carry voltages of many thousands of volts; and lesser electrostatic voltages are often present on human fingers. There is also the danger of induced voltages from the a.c. mains supply.

Voltages of this type cause no damage to bipolar transistors or junction FET's because these devices have enough leakage resistance to discharge the voltage harmlessly. The high resistance of the MOSFET gate, however, ensures that electrostatic voltages cannot be discharged in this way, so that damage to the gate of a MOSFET is always possible.

The precautions which must be taken include the following:—
1. Always keep new MOSFET's with conductive plastic foam wrapped round their leads until after they have been soldered in place.
2. Always short the leads of a MOSFET together before unsoldering it.
3. Never touch MOSFET leads with your fingers.
4. Never plug a MOSFET into a holder when the circuit is switched on.

Exercise 3.3
Using a 2N3819 junction FET, connect the circuit shown in Fig. 3.10. The milliammeter measures the current through the channel, and the voltmeter measures the (negative) bias on the gate.

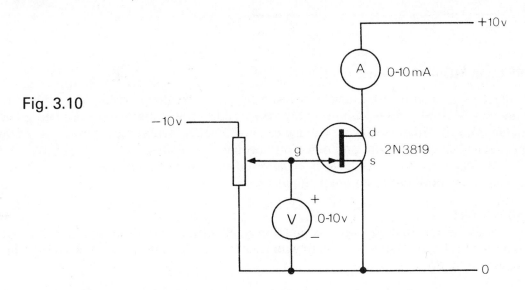

Fig. 3.10

For the bias voltages listed, fill in the readings of current. Find also the *cut-off voltage*, which is the gate voltage at which channel current flow just reaches zero.

FET's can be used in circuits similar to those in which bipolar transistors are used, but they give low voltage gain and are only used when their peculiar advantages are required. These are:—

1. FET's have a very high input resistance at the gate — a useful feature in voltmeter amplifiers.

2. FET's perform very well as switches, with channel resistance switching between a few hundred ohms and several megohms as gate voltage is varied.

3. The graph of channel current I_{ds} plotted against V_{gs} — the voltage between the gate and the source — is noticeably curved in a shape called a *square law* (see Fig. 3.11). This type of characteristic is particularly useful for signal mixers in superheterodyne receivers.

Double-gate MOSFET's are used as mixers and as RF amplifiers in FM receivers. The shape of their characteristic also gives less distortion in power amplifiers, and high-power FET's are now available for use in high-quality audio equipment.

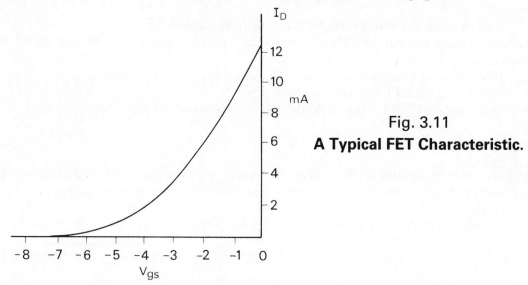

Fig. 3.11
A Typical FET Characteristic.

FET and MOSFET Failure

Failure of a junction FET can be caused by either an open-circuit or a short-circuit junction. MOSFET failure is almost always caused by breakdown of the insulating silicon oxide layer. In either case, gate voltage can no longer control current flow in the channel between source and drain, and pinch-off becomes impossible.

If very large currents have been allowed to flow between source and drain, the channel may burn out to an open circuit.

SUMMARY

FET's are devices that depend on a junction action different to that of bipolar transistors. Junction FET's are usually operated with their single junction reverse-biased (*i.e.,* in the depletion mode).

MOSFET's have almost infinite gate resistance, and the leads must not be touched unless the gate is first shorted to the other two electrodes.

FET's are used in applications where their high input resistance, good switching characteristics and low-noise factor outweigh their poor voltage gain.

3. THE UNIJUNCTION

The unijunction has a construction rather similar to that of a junction FET, but with the junction formed about midway along the silicon bar. When the bar is connected across a supply voltage (with the voltage at Base 1 always lower than that at Base 2), the resistance of the bar will cause potential divider action, so that the voltage of the N-part of the junction (assuming that an N-channel is used) will be somewhere between zero volts and supply voltage, according to the position of the junction.

If the channel is only lightly doped, the resistance will be high, and very little current will flow when a voltage is placed across the channel.

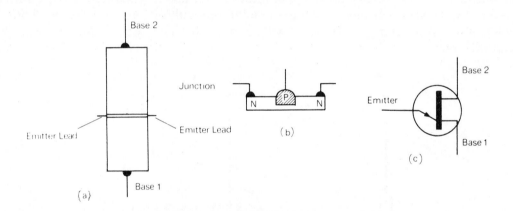

Fig. 3.12   The UNIJUNCTION.

(a) Schematic. (b) The Junction in profile. (c) Symbol.

When the emitter terminal is at the same voltage as the Base 1 terminal (which is always, it will be remembered, lower than B2), the junction is reverse-biased because the part of the junction lying in the channel is at a higher voltage than the emitter.

If emitter voltage be now raised slowly, current will start to flow across the junction when emitter voltage is about 0.5V above the voltage at the N-part of the junction (again assuming an N-channel unijunction).

When this happens, carriers (electrons in this case) enter the channel, making it a good conductor. Current can now pass freely between emitter and Base 1, and also between B2 and B1. This conductivity continues until emitter voltage is again reduced to almost zero voltage.

The unijunction is used to generate trigger pulses from slowly-changing waveforms, or as an oscillator generating sawtooth waveforms or pulses. It is mainly used in the circuits used to trigger thyristors (see below).

The voltage needed at the emitter for the unijunction to start conducting is called the *striking voltage.* The ratio of the values: $\dfrac{\text{Striking Voltage}}{\text{Supply Voltage}}$ is called the *intrinsic stand-off ratio,* and is a constant in a given unijunction because it depends only on the position of the junction along the bar.

For example, if a unijunction supplied with 6V between B1 and B2 triggers on 4V, then its stand-off ratio is 4/6, equal to 2/3 or 0.67. When 12V is connected between B1 and B2, the trigger voltage will be $2/3 \times 12 = 8V$.

When a unijunction has to be replaced, the replacement must possess the same values of maximum voltage and current, and the same intrinsic stand-off ratio.

Exercise 3.4
Connect the circuit of Fig. 3.13, and measure the supply voltage *E.*

Starting at zero volts, measure the emitter voltage and raise its value slowly until the unijunction triggers, causing the milliammeter suddenly to give a reading. Note the reading of the voltmeter just before the triggering, and calculate the value of the intrinsic stand-off ratio.

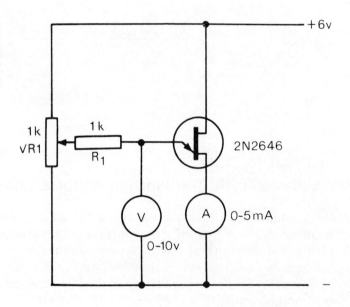

Fig. 3.13

Now change the value of the supply voltage and repeat your readings. Is the same value of intrinsic stand-off ratio obtained with the new supply voltage?

4. THE THYRISTOR

The thyristor is a switching device whose symbol and schematic construction are shown in Fig. 3.14.

When gate voltage is zero, the device offers high resistance irrespective of the polarity of the anode-to-cathode voltage, because there is always one *PN* junction with reverse bias. Even when a thyristor is forward-biased, with the anode positive and the cathode negative, it will only be driven into conduction when a short positive pulse is applied to its gate.

Once it has been switched on in this way, the thyristor will remain conducting until either:

(a) The voltage between anode and cathode falls to a small fraction of a volt; or

(b) Current flow between anode and cathode falls to a very low value.

The important ratings for a thyristor are its maximum average current flow, its peak inverse voltage, and its values of gate-firing voltage and current. A small thyristor will fire at a very small value of gate current, but a large one calls for considerably greater firing current (100μA or more).

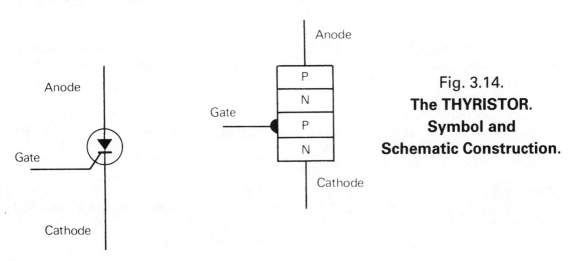

Fig. 3.14.
The THYRISTOR.
Symbol and
Schematic Construction.

Exercise 3.5

Connect the circuit of Fig. 3.15. Any small 1-ampere thyristor will do for the job. The purpose of the lamp bulb is to indicate when the thyristor has switched on.

Use a d.c. supply as shown, and measure voltage and current at the gate just as the thyristor fires — noting also that both values change after the thyristor has fired.

After the lamp lights, disconnect the gate circuit, and note that this has no effect.

Switch off the power supply, and then switch on again. The lamp will not now light because the thyristor has switched off.

Repeat the operation, this time using an unsmoothed supply. The thyristor now switches off when the gate voltage is switched off because the unsmoothed supply reaches zero voltage 100 times per second (assuming a full-wave rectified 50 Hz supply).

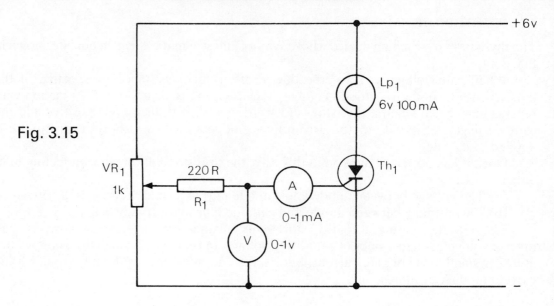

Fig. 3.15

Thyristors are used for power control, using either a.c. or an unsmoothed rectified supply. By being made to fire at different parts of the cycle, the thyristor can be made to conduct for different percentages of the cycle, thus controlling average current flow through the load.

An alternative method used in furnace control allows the thyristor to conduct for several cycles of a.c., and then to cut off the current flow for several more cycles. By altering the ratio: $\dfrac{\text{Cycles Conducting}}{\text{Cycles Non-Conducting}}$, average power can be controlled.

Exercise 3.6
Connect the thyristor circuit of Fig. 3.16 and switch on. Use the potentiometer to control lamp brightness by altering the time in the cycle at which the thyristor fires.

Note that an unsmoothed full-wave rectified supply is essential.

Thyristor Failure

Failure of a thyristor can be caused by an open-circuit gate, or by internal short-circuits.

When the gate is open-circuit, the thyristor will fail to conduct at any gate voltage. When an internal short circuit is present, the thyristor acts like a diode, conducting whenever the anode is more than 0.6V positive to the cathode, so making control impossible.

A completely short-circuit thyristor is able to conduct in either direction, with similar total loss of control.

Most thyristor circuits include inductors in series with the anode, in order to suppress the radio-frequency interference which could be caused by the sudden switch-on of the thyristor.

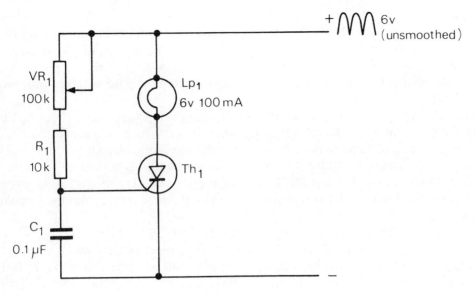

Fig. 3.16

5. THE DIAC

A diac is a triggering diode which is often used in the gate circuit of a thyristor or triac (see below).

At low voltages, a diac will not conduct in either direction, but at a triggering voltage of either polarity it becomes a good conductor in both directions.

When a diac is used, the gate of the thyristor can be connected to the cathode by a low-value resistor to avoid accidental triggering. In addition, if the triggering waveform rises slowly, the diac will ensure that the thyristor is switched on by a sharp pulse of current, so avoiding uncertain triggering times.

The symbol for, and a typical use of, the diac are shown in Fig. 3.17.

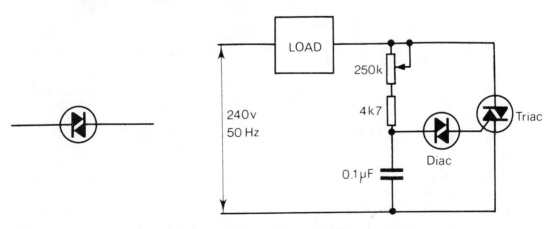

Fig. 3.17   **The DIAC. Symbol and Typical Connection.**

6. THE TRIAC

A triac is a two-way thyristor which, when triggered, will conduct in either direction. The terminals are B1, B2 and gate (the terms "anode" and "cathode" cannot be used because the current can flow in either direction). The gate can be triggered by a pulse of either polarity, but the most reliable triggering is achieved when the gate is pulsed positive with respect to B1.

In most triac circuits, B1 and B2 have alternating voltages applied to them, so that the gate must receive the same waveform as B1 when it is not being triggered.

To trigger the gate, a pulse must be added to the waveform already present, and this is most easily done by using a pulse transformer driven by a trigger circuit.

Fig. 3.18 shows the symbol for a triac, and part of a typical triggering circuit. A transformer is used to isolate the triac, which works at line voltage, from the low-voltage control circuit.

The causes of failure in triacs are the same as they are for thyristors.

The advantages of using thyristors and triacs for power control are:

1. Both thyristor and triac are either completely off, with no current flowing, or fully on, with only a small voltage between the terminals. Either way, very little power is dissipated in the semiconductor.

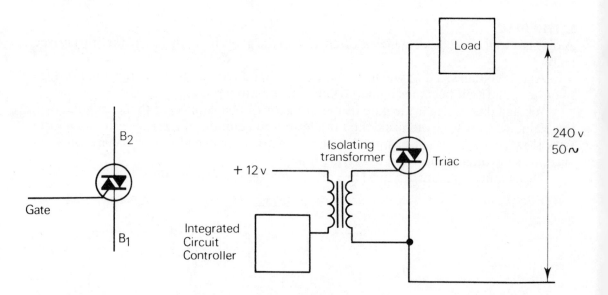

Fig. 3.18 **The TRIAC.** Symbol and Typical Connection.

2. Operation can be either at line or at higher frequencies — unlike relays or similar electromechanical switches.

3. Thyristors and triacs are *self-latching* — which means that they stay conducting once they have been triggered. A relay, by contrast, needs a current passed continuously through its coil to keep it switched over.

SUMMARY
Unijunctions, thyristors, diacs and triacs are all switching devices which switch suddenly from a non-conducting state to a conducting state.

Unijunctions and diacs are used to provide trigger pulses for thyristors and triacs, which in turn are used to control power in a load.

The supply for thyristor circuits is usually unsmoothed rectified current. Triacs operate from an a.c. supply.

7. INTRODUCING INTEGRATED CIRCUITS

The actual size of the silicon chip in a transistor is very small compared to the size of the transistor case; and the size of the active part of the chip is smaller still.

Transistors are made by processes resembling photographic printing; and once master drawings have been made, it is as easy to "print" a hundred transistors on to a silicon chip as it is to print one.

The several steps in the process used to make transistors can also be used to form resistors and capacitors — of small values only, it is true — on to the silicon chip. The result is that complete circuits can be made in one set of manufacturing operations which are essentially similar to the set of steps used to make transistors alone. Such circuits are called **integrated circuits** (**IC**'s for short), or thin-film circuits.

Integrated circuits can be made exceedingly small. A photograph of a small part of the surface of an IC used to operate a pocket calculator (Fig. 3.19) is highly magnified. The actual size of the portion of the IC shown is about that of one of the lower-case letters used to print this page.

IC's can be soldered into normal printed circuit boards; but for some military and industrial uses, thick-film circuits are used. These are like miniature printed-circuit boards, only with printed silicon chips and other miniature components soldered or welded in place, and resistors or capacitors formed by the metallic films on the boards. The differences between thick-film and thin-film (IC) circuits are:

1. Thin-film IC's are formed on silicon and contain transistors, resistors and capacitors formed in silicon.

2. Thick films are made of a plate of conductive metal such as nickel, stuck or welded to a material such as glass or sapphire, with transistors or IC chips attached.

3. Thin-film IC's are usually made so that they can be used in a great variety of applications, while thick-film circuits are more likely to be "dedicated" — or made for one purpose only.

Handling IC's

IC's may be either bipolar or metal-oxide-silicon; and the handling precautions which must be taken with MOS transistors apply equally to MOS IC's.

The maximum working voltages for IC's are generally lower than they are for bipolar transistors; and maximum power dissipation is usually low except in the case of specially-designed power output IC's. In some cases, supply voltages must be carefully regulated. For example, IC's of the logic TTL family need a 5V supply which must never fall below 4.8V nor rise above 5.4V.

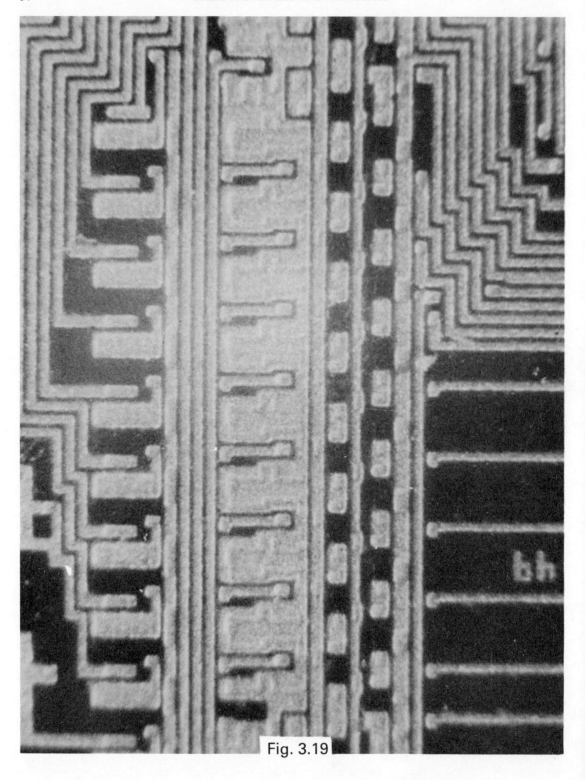

Fig. 3.19

Other types need balanced power supplies, such as ± 9V, which have to be provided from suitable rectifier circuits.

The most common form of IC package is the **DIL**, a rectangular slab with two lines of pins sticking out on either side of it. The name is composed of the initials of the words *dual-in-line,* referring to the two rows of pins. Pin numbers in common use are 8, 14, 16 and 24 — with a few large IC's (mainly designed for computer use) having greater numbers of pins.

Pin spacings are always multiples of 2.5 mm apart (this is referred to as a *2.5 mm matrix*), so that they fit exactly into the standard spacing of the holes in printed circuit boards. Great care must be taken when inserting pins to avoid bending them in any direction.

The pin-numbering system shown in Fig. 3.20 always starts from the *identifying mark* and runs in the way illustrated, even for DIL IC's containing many more pins than the 8-pin and the 14-pin IC's depicted.

Most IC's cannot be easily tested before being soldered into a circuit, so it is important that they be bought from reputable sources. The circuit into which the IC is to be soldered should be checked carefully for open circuits or accidental short circuits. Note that, with printed circuit tracks only 2.5 mm apart, small splashes of solder can easily cause a short between tracks.

When an IC is soldered into place, its pin No. 1 should be soldered first, then the circuit connections checked. Its opposite pin is then soldered in, and the circuit checked again to make quite sure that the IC has been put in the right way round. If the connections are incorrect, it is possible to remove the IC quite easily at this stage.

If the circuit seems satisfactory, the remaining pins are then soldered in.

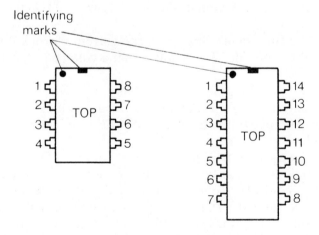

Fig. 3.20 **PIN-NUMBERING** Systems for Integrated Circuits.

If a faulty IC has to be removed from a circuit — and the job should not be attempted until it is quite certain that the IC really *is* faulty — the easiest method is to cut off all the pins, remove the body of the IC, then unsolder each pin, pulling the pin out with tweezers while the soldering iron is used to melt the solder. When all this has been done, there is at least no chance that the faulty IC will ever again be mistaken for a good one!

Alternative methods which preserve the pins for future use employ solder-removing tools such as solderwick or solder pumps. By these methods the solder is removed from the pins so that the IC can be lifted out intact. This method should be adopted if there is any doubt whether it is the IC or the circuit itself which is at fault.

If the IC is of the MOS type, soft copper wire should always be wrapped around the pins before de-soldering begins.

When there is an IC failure, it is usually fairly simple to find out which IC has failed, but less easy to find out why. Every IC will have some d.c. bias voltage which can be measured. If bias voltages are correct, and if the correct input signals are being applied, then the correct output signals must appear if the IC is operating correctly.

The exceptions to this rule are some power-output or stabiliser IC's which the temperature becomes too high. If a fault is suspected in an IC of this type, testing should be deferred until the IC has cooled.

In many respects, the servicing of IC's is rather easier than is the servicing of discrete transistor equipment.

Magnetic-Dependent Semiconductors

When a current-carrying conductor is exposed to a magnetic field, a mechanical reaction occurs which tends to cause the conductor to move. This is the principle of the electric motor which was described in Part 1. The direction of the motion can be predicted from Fleming's Left-Hand Rule for motors.

If the conductor is *prevented* from moving, however, the current carriers flowing within the conductor are deflected to one side. The result is that a voltage is developed across the width of the conductor itself.

In normal conductors this effect is of no practical importance; but when *a magnetic field* is applied to semiconductor materials, the voltage so generated becomes significant. It is put to practical use in a group of semiconductors called **Hall-Effect Devices,** illustrated in schematic form in Fig. 3.21 below.

A Hall-Effect device consists of a very small (about 2mm × 2mm × 0.5mm) slab of gallium arsenide, indium antimonide or silicon on to which two pairs of electrodes are evaporated, as shown in Fig. 3.21. A control current I and a magnetic field B are applied as shown, and the Hall Voltage V_H is developed at right angles to both of them. The value of V_H is proportional to both the current I and the strength of the magnetic field B, the constant of proportionality depending on the dimensions and nature of the semiconductor material.

Given a constant current, the Hall Voltage is directly proportional to the strength of the magnetic field. The first and most obvious application for the device is therefore the measurement of the field strengths of both permanent magnets and electro-magnets. But

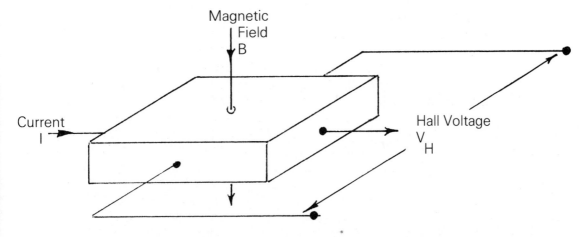

Fig 3.21   **Schematic Diagram of a Hall-Effect Device.**

it is also used in conjunction with switching transistors in d.c. electric motors, where it can replace the mechanical brush gear which is so prone to wear and to the generation of radio interference by arcing. The device can also be used in contact-less switches, where the movement of a permanent magnet sets up the Hall voltage, which in turn triggers a semiconductor switch.

Magnetic-Dependent Resistors

When the application of the magnetic field in the Hall-Effect device deflects the current carriers to one side of the conductor, they are caused to flow through a smaller cross-sectional area. This increases the effective resistance of the device, and so reduces current flow. The characteristic of a typical magnetic-dependent resistor is shown in Fig. 3.22 below.

Over a normal range of magnetic fields strengths, device resistance can in this way be made to vary by a factor of about 5.

One particularly useful application of a magnetic-dependent resistor is in the "clamp-on" type of current meter used to measure current flow in power supplies drawing power directly from the electrical mains.

SUMMARY

IC's are etched on to thin silicon plates in the same way as are transistors, but in such a way that a complete circuit is made in one manufacturing process.

Thick film circuits are manufactured from metal film deposited on insulators, with resistors and capacitors formed in place. The active components (transistors, IC's, etc.) have to be added later.

Magnetic-dependent devices, made by using only standard semiconductor technology, provide a very reliable replacement for mechanical switch contacts, and also provide a method of measuring the strength of magnetic fields.

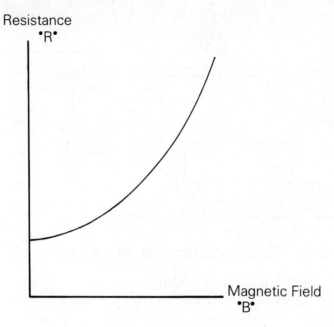

Fig. 3.22
Characteristic of a Typical
Magnetic-Dependent Resistor.

CHAPTER 4

Voltage Amplifiers

The bipolar transistor and the FET both control the current flow at their output terminals (collector and drain respectively); and in both cases this current at the output can be controlled by the voltage at the input.

The ratio:—

$$\frac{\text{Change of Current at Output}}{\text{Change of Voltage at Input}} \text{ (given a constant supply voltage)}$$

is called the **mutual conductance** of the particular bipolar transistor or FET to which it applies. Its symbol is g_m. The values of mutual conductance obtainable from bipolar transistors are much greater than are those from FET's. In the mutual conductance graph shown in Fig. 4.1, for instance, a 30 mV input wave gives a 1 mA current flow at the

output. The mutual conductance g_m is therefore $\dfrac{1}{0.03}$ = 33.3 mA/V.

Collector
Current
(mA)

Output Current Wave
1mA, peak to peak

1.5

1.0

0.5

.53 .56 .59   Base Voltage (volts)

Input Voltage wave
0.03 v, peak to peak

Fig. 4.1

The method of operation is as follows. A signal voltage, alternating from one peak of voltage to the other, at the input produces a signal current, alternating from one peak of current to the other, at the output. To convert this signal current into a signal voltage again, a load is connected between the output terminal and the supply voltage. In a d.c. or an audio amplifier, a resistor can be used as the load; but for i.f. or r.f. amplifier circuits a tuned circuit (which behaves like a resistor at its tuned frequency) is used instead.

When the device in question is connected in the common-emitter mode, the use of a load resistor causes the output voltage to be inverted compared to the input voltage. A higher steady voltage at the input causes a greater current flow at the output. A larger voltage is therefore dropped across the load resistor, which causes the output voltage to be lower.

Any amplifying stage can give current gain, voltage gain or power gain — the amounts of gain which can be obtained depending on the way the circuits are connected. Fig. 4.2 shows the three possible amplifying connections of a transistor, with their relative gain values (bias components not shown).

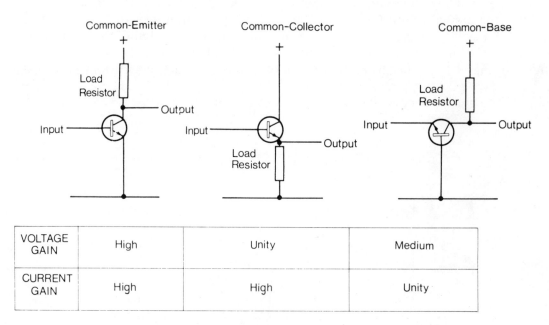

	Common-Emitter	Common-Collector	Common-Base
VOLTAGE GAIN	High	Unity	Medium
CURRENT GAIN	High	High	Unity

Fig. 4.2

Note that circuits using bipolar or field effect transistors give power gain — the amount of this gain being calculated by multiplying voltage gain by current gain.

The Transfer Characteristic

The behaviour of an amplifier can be clearly read from a graph of its output voltage or current plotted against its input voltage or current (for given values of load resistance and supply voltage). For example, the transfer characteristic of a small bipolar transistor is shown in Fig. 4.3. An input current wave of 50μA peak-to-peak produces an output current wave of 4mA peak-to-peak. The current gain h_{fe} of the transistor under these conditions is thus

$$\frac{\text{Collector Current Swing}}{\text{Base Current Swing}} = \frac{4\text{mA}}{50\mu\text{A}} = 80.$$

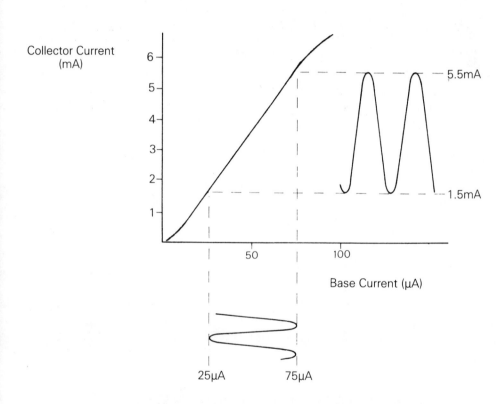

Fig. 4.3

The voltage wave produced is in this case an exact copy of the input wave, because that part of the graph which represents the values of voltage and current is a straight line. Because a straight-line characteristic produces a perfect copy, such an amplifier is called a **linear amplifier**. If the input signal had been greater, with peak values 0 and 30μA, the output signal would not have been a perfect copy of the input wave because the output voltage cannot exceed 6V even when the input current changes from 17μA to 30μA. The output signal would therefore be distorted because the part of the characteristic now being used would not be a section of a straight line.

Fig. 4.4 shows the plots of the output current/input **voltage** characteristics of (*a*) a bipolar transistor and (*b*) a FET. The shape of these characteristics shows that reasonably good linear amplification is possible only if a small part of the characteristic is selected for use. It is not, for example, possible to use an input voltage of less than 0.6V for the bipolar transistor.

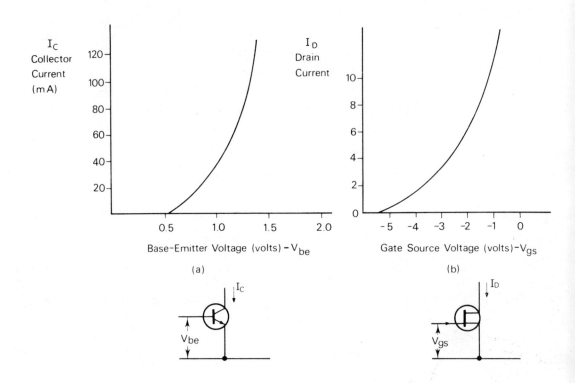

Fig. 4.4   The MUTUAL CHARACTERISTICS of (a) a typical Bipolar Transistor, and (b) a typical Junction FET.

In practice, however, these two latter transfer characteristics are seldom drawn — the more usual type of information given being the *output characteristic*. In Fig. 4.5 every line is the graph of I_c/V_c for a given base current I_b. The difference in spacing shows that amplification will be non-linear. In other words, if the output characteristic lines are drawn for equal changes of input voltage or current, the unequal spacing of the lines indicates that the transfer characteristic must be curved, producing the effects already noted.

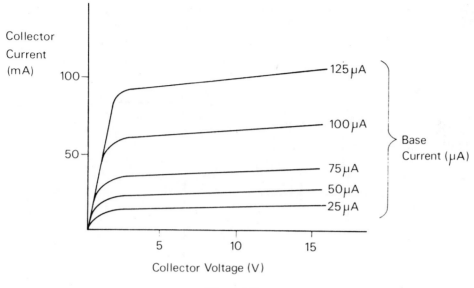

Fig. 4.5

Bias

The mutual characteristics of the bipolar transistor shown in Fig. 4.4(a) make it clear that if such a transistor is to be used as a linear amplifier, the output current must never cut off nor must the output voltage be allowed to reach zero (its so-called *bottomed condition*).

Ideally, when no signal input is applied, output current should be exactly half-way between these two conditions. This can be achieved by **biasing** — *i.e.*, by supplying a steady d.c. input which ensures a correct level of current flow at the output. A correctly-biased amplifier will always deliver a larger undistorted signal than will an incorrectly-biased one.

A correctly-biased amplifier operating in such conditions, with the output current flowing for the whole of the input cycle, is said to be operating under *Class A conditions*.

Exercise 4.1

Connect the circuit shown in Fig. 4.6, in which Tr1 can be any medium-current silicon NPN transistor such as 2N697, 2N1711, 2N2219 or BFY60. Set the signal generator to deliver a signal of 50 mV peak-to-peak at 1kHz when connected to the amplifier input. Connect the oscilloscope to the output terminals, with the Y-input of the oscilloscope to Point X. Set the oscilloscope Y-input to 1V/cm and the timebase control to 1 ms/cm, and switch on the oscilloscope. When the trace is visible, adjust the potentiometer VR_1 to its minimum voltage position, and switch on the amplifier circuit.

Note that there is no output from the amplifier because it is incorrectly biased. Gradually increase the bias voltage by adjusting VR_1 until a waveform trace appears. Draw the wave-shape.

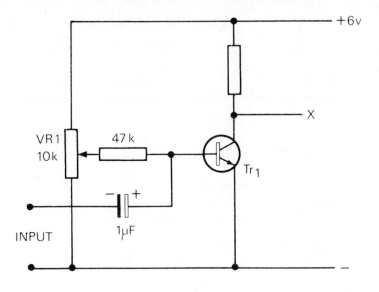

Fig. 4.6

Continue to adjust the bias voltage until the waveform seen on the oscilloscope screen is a pure sine-wave — it may be necessary to adjust the amplitude of the input wave to achieve this.

Then increase the bias still further until distortion becomes noticeable again, and sketch this waveform also. You will see that with too little bias the amplifier cuts off, causing the top of the waveform to flatten. With too much bias, the amplifier bottoms, causing the bottom of the waveform to flatten.

SUMMARY

All transistor-type amplifier circuits produce a gain in power, and both voltage gain and current gain can be obtained.

Gain is obtained by generating an output waveform under the control of the input waveform, and the transfer characteristic is the graph of output plotted against input.

If the graph of the transfer characteristic is a straight line for the quantities being plotted (power, voltage or current), the amplifier is *a linear amplifier of that quantity,* and the output wave will be a perfect copy of the input wave, with no distortion.

Bias Circuits

Three types of bias circuit are illustrated in Fig. 4.7. The simplest uses a single resistor connected between the supply voltage and the base of the transistor (fig. 4.7(a)). This type of bias is seldom used for linear amplifier stages nowadays because it is difficult to find a suitable value of bias resistor. In this simple type of system, the value of resistor for correct biasing depends on the value of current gain (h_{fe}) of the transistor, so that a bias resistor suitable for one transistor will not work properly with another even if it is of the same type number.

Moreover, the value of bias resistor may be critical, so that one preferred value of resistance is too low and the next in the series too high.

The simple bias system is unsuitable if the transistor has to work at varying temperatures, because the voltage needed between the base and the emitter for a given collector current decreases as the temperature of a silicon transistor rises. With the simple system of bias, this change in forward voltage causes more base current to flow, and so more collector current flows as the temperature increases. Unless collector current is limited by a load resistor, the additional current will heat the transistor, so causing current flow to increase still further until the transistor is destroyed.

This process, called *thermal runaway,* is much less common nowadays, when use of silicon transistors is so general, than it was when germanium transistors found many applications.

The circuit shown in Fig. 4.7(b) represents a considerable improvement, because the bias resistor is returned to the collector of the transistor rather than to the fixed-voltage supply line. This small change makes the bias to some extent self-adjusting, and the bias is now said to be *stabilised.*

The connection of the bias resistor as shown causes d.c. feedback, which means that the level of d.c. voltage at the collector affects the amount of d.c. bias current at the base. See what happens in two opposite cases. *First,* a change either in the transistor itself or in the load which causes collector current to increase will, because of the presence of the load

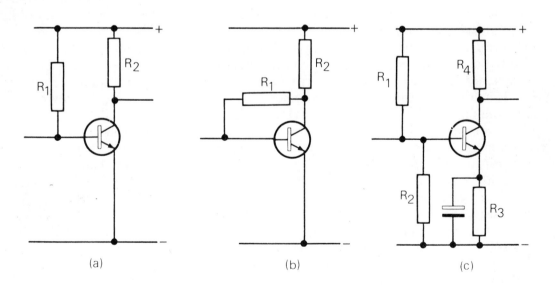

(a)   (b)   (c)

Fig. 4.7
BIAS SYSTEMS.
(a) **Simple.** (b) **Current Feedback type.** (c) **Fixed Voltage type.**

resistor, cause collector voltage to drop. By Ohm's Law, this will reduce current flow through the base resistor, so reducing base current, and so reducing collector current back to near its original value. *Alternatively,* a change causing collector current to drop will make collector voltage rise, so passing more current through the bias resistor, causing more base current to flow, thereby increasing collector current back to nearly its original value.

All negative-feedback systems act in a similar way, tending to keep conditions in an amplifier unchanged despite other variations. A.c. feedback and its effects will be considered later on.

The third bias circuit, shown in Fig. 4.7(c), is the most commonly-used of all. A pair of resistors is connected as a potential divider to set the voltage at the base terminal, and a resistor placed in series with the emitter controls emitter current flow by d.c. negative feedback. Note the emitter current is practically equal to the collector current flow ($I_c = I_e + I_b$, but I_b is very small).

In this type of circuit, the replacement of one transistor by another has little effect on the level of steady bias voltage at the collector. This biasing arrangement is therefore ideal for use in mass-produced circuits which must behave correctly even when fitted with transistors having a wide range of values of h_{fe}.

Exercise 4.2

Set up the circuit shown in Fig. 4.8(a), preferably on a suitable "breadboard". (This is a board on which experimental circuits can be mounted for training or testing purposes by plugging the relevant components into appropriate holes in the board. At the back of the board is an assembly of spring contacts interconnected in groups, which form the required circuit connections. Since no soldering is required, all components can be pulled out when circuits have been tested, and the board is ready for re-use. The so-called "Euro-Breadboard" supplied by David George Sales (Crayford) fulfils most training needs).

Switch on and adjust the potentiometer until collector voltage is exactly half the supply voltage. Note this value of resistance.

Now connect a 470k resistor in parallel with the bias resistor. Note the new value of collector voltage. Remove the 470k resistor, and connect a 6k8 resistor in parallel with the load resistor. Note the value of collector voltage now. Remove the 6k8 resistor, and replace the transistor with another of the same type, again noting the collector voltage.

These three readings show how the bias voltage has been altered by changes in the bias resistor, the load resistor and the transistor respectively.

Now set up the bias system shown in Fig. 4.8(b) and again adjust the potentiometer until collector voltage is exactly half the supply voltage. Note this value.

As before, connect a 470k resistor in parallel with the bias potentiometer and note the collector voltage. Then remove the 470k resistor, and connect a 6k8 resistor in parallel with the load resistor, noting the effect on the collector voltage. Finally, remove the 6k8 resistor, and find the effect on collector voltage of replacing the transistor. Have the changes in collector voltage been as large as they were in the first case?

Finally, set up the bias system shown in Fig. 4.8(c). Measure the collector voltage, then apply the same tests as before and note the effects. Try out several types of silicon transistors in the circuit, noting the collector voltage for each. Does this circuit stabilise bias voltage well?

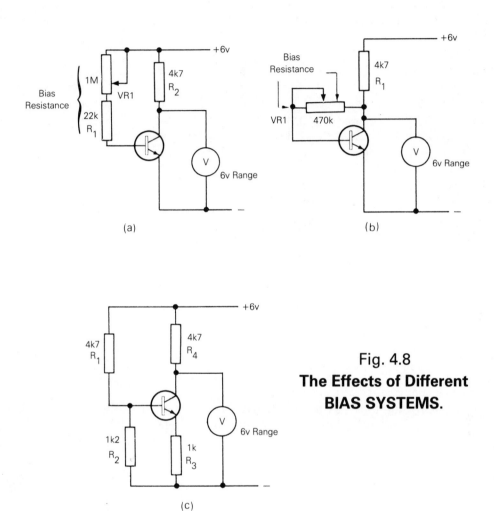

Fig. 4.8
The Effects of Different BIAS SYSTEMS.

Fig 4.9 illustrates the circuit of a junction FET and shows the bias method which is used for a FET in the depletion mode. (MOSFET's use the same type of bias circuit also).

For correct bias, the voltage of the gate should be negative with respect to the source voltage — or, to put the same thing another way, the source voltage must be positive with respect to the gate voltage. In this circuit the positive voltage is obtained from the voltage drop across the resistor R_3 in series with the source. The gate voltage is kept at earth (ground level, or zero volts) by the resistor R_1, which needs to have a very large value since no current flows in the gate circuit.

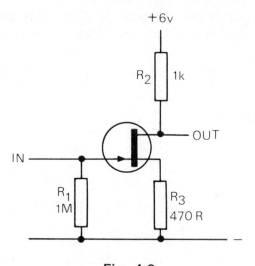

Fig. 4.9
BIASING CIRCUIT
for a Junction FET.

It will be seen that the biasing of a FET is considerably simpler than is the biasing of a bipolar transistor.

SUMMARY
The purpose of biasing a transistor is to set its output current to a value which permits the best use to be made of its transfer characteristic.

For a linear amplifier having a resistive load, the most useful bias setting is to a collector voltage close to half the supply voltage (*Class A*).

The biasing method chosen must be stable, lest the bias setting be upset by small changes in component values.

Bias Failure

Bias failure can be caused by either open-circuit or short-circuit bias components.

In any of the circuits shown in Fig. 4.7, if a s/c develops across the resistor R_1, the large bias current that will flow in consequence will cause the collector voltage to bottom, and may burn out the base-emitter junction. If the base-emitter junction thus becomes o/c, collector voltage will rise to supply voltage, so that the same fault can be the cause of either symptom.

If R_1 becomes o/c, there is no bias supply and the collector voltage cuts off, so that collector voltage equals supply voltage.

In the case of the circuit in Fig. 4.7(c), faults in resistors R_2 and R_3 can also affect the bias. The table below summarises the possible faults and their effects.

Fault	Collector Voltage	Emitter Voltage
R_2 o/c	Low	High
s/c across R_2	High	Zero
R_3 o/c	High	High
s/c across R_3	Low	Zero

Gain and Bandwidth

The voltage gain **(G)** of an amplifier is defined as:—

$$G = \frac{\text{Signal Voltage at Output}}{\text{Signal Voltage at Input}}$$

with both signal voltages measured in the same way (either both r.m.s. or both peak-to-peak). This quantity G is an important measure of the efficiency of the amplifier and is often expressed in decibels by means of the equation:—

$$dB = 20 \log G$$

Example
Find the gain of an amplifier in which a 30 mV peak-to-peak input signal produces a 2V peak-to-peak output signal.

Solution
Insert the data in the equation: $G = \dfrac{\text{Output Signal}}{\text{Input Signal}}$

Then
$$G = \frac{2\,000}{30} = 66.7$$

Note that the 2V must be converted into 2 000 mV, so that both input and output signals are quoted in the same units.

Expressing the same answer in decibels:—

$$G = 20 \log 66.7 = 36.5 \text{ dB}.$$

The example shows the superiority of the decibel method of expressing gain. A decrease in gain from 66.7 to 60 might seem significant, but the same decrease expressed in decibels is only from 36.5 dB to 35.5 dB — a change of 1 dB, which is the smallest change of gain that can be detected by the ear when the amplifier is in use. Measurements of gain expressed in decibels can therefore show whether changes of gain are significant or not. Figures of voltage gain by themselves are often misleading for this purpose.

Voltage amplifiers do not have the same value of gain at all signal frequencies. Fig. 4.10 shows the components in a single-stage transistor amplifier which determine frequency response. (C_4 is shown dotted because it consists of stray capacitances and is not an actual physical component).

In the circuit, C_1 prevents d.c. from the signal source from affecting the bias at the

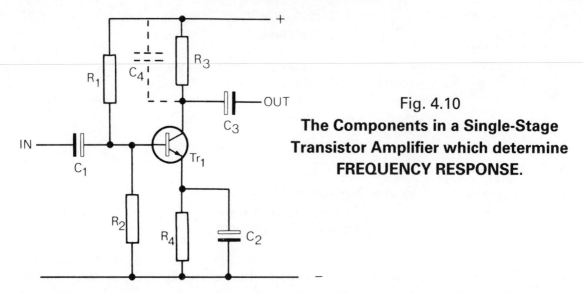

Fig. 4.10

The Components in a Single-Stage Transistor Amplifier which determine FREQUENCY RESPONSE.

base of the transistor, and C_3 prevents d.c. from its collector from affecting the next stage. The circuit can therefore give no voltage gain for d.c.; and the amount of gain it can give at low a.c. frequencies is inevitably limited by the action of the capacitors C_1 and C_3. (Gain will also be affected by C_2, because this capacitor bypasses the negative feedback action of R_4 for a.c. signals only).

Again, at the high end of the frequency scale, the stray capacitances which would then be present at the collector of the transistor and in any circuit connected through C_3 — they are represented by C_4 connected across the load resistor — act to bypass high-frequency signals, so that gain decreases at these frequencies also. Only in the medium range of signal frequencies most commonly used is the gain given by this circuit configuration constant.

A typical curve of gain (in decibels) plotted against frequency for such an amplifier is shown in Fig. 4.11. Note that the frequency scale is logarithmic, in that tenfold frequency

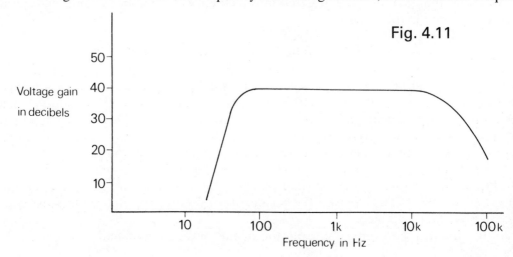

Fig. 4.11

steps occupy equal lengths of horizontal scale. This type of scale is necessary to show the full frequency range of an amplifier.

When a tuned circuit is used as the output load of an amplifier (Fig. 4.12), the shape of the gain/frequency graph becomes more peaked. The reason is that the tuned circuit presents a high resistance to the signal at the frequency of resonance (f_r).

At resonance, this resistance has a value of $\dfrac{L}{CR}$ ohms, where L is in henries, C in farads, and R is the resistance of the coil expressed in ohms. This value $\dfrac{L}{CR}$ is called the *dynamic resistance* of the tuned circuit.

At all frequencies other than resonance, the load has a considerably lower value of resistance and acts instead like an impedance — with the result that voltage and current become out of phase with one another.

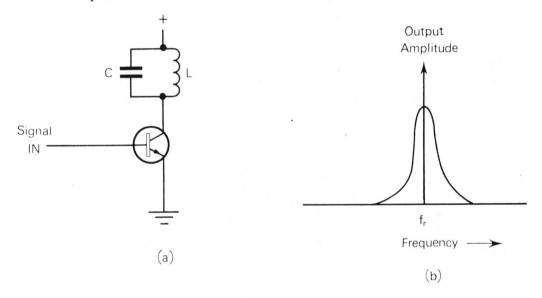

(a)

(b)

Fig. 4.12   **A TUNED AMPLIFIER, with Frequency Response.**

In such a tuned amplifier, the gain at the resonant frequency is often controlled by an *automatic gain control (AGC)* voltage. This voltage is applied at the base, either opposing or adding to the existing d.c. bias. What is known as *reverse AGC* uses a d.c. bias voltage that reduces normal bias current; while *forward AGC* uses a bias voltage that increases the normal bias current. The type of AGC used depends on the type of transistor and the circuit of which it is a component.

To give forward AGC, a resistor is included in series with the load — but bypassed by a capacitor, so that signal current does not flow through it — and the transistor is so designed that gain is much lower at low collector voltages. Increasing the bias current then lowers collector voltage and decreases the gain.

Most transistors, however, give greater gain at higher bias currents (given unchanged collector voltage), and so need to use reverse AGC.

Exercise 4.3

Construct the circuit shown in Fig. 4.13, in which Tr1 can be any medium-current NPN silicon transistor such as 2N697, 2N1711, 2N2219 or BFY 50. Measure the collector voltage and note its value.

Connect the output of the signal generator to Point A, and its earth return to Point C. The Y-input of an oscilloscope should also be connected to Point A. Switch on all circuits, and adjust signal generator output to give a 1 kHz, 30 mV peak-to-peak signal at Point A.

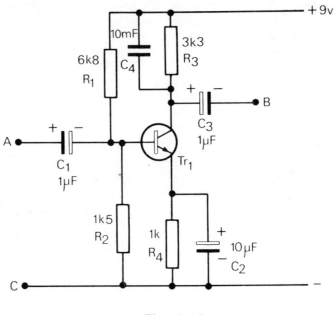

Fig. 4.13

Now connect the Y-input of the oscilloscope to Point B, and read the peak-to-peak value of the output signal. Calculate the gain, convert it to decibels, and record this value as the gain of 1 kHz. If the output wave is noticeably distorted (i.e., flattened at either peak), reduce the amplitude of the signal generator output until a well-shaped sine-wave appears at the output. Note the new value of input signal needed.

Now multiply your known figure of output voltage at 1 kHz by 0.71, and reduce the output frequency of the signal generator until the output voltage reaches this lower value. Record the signal generator frequency required to achieve this, and call it f_1.

Increase signal generator frequency again until you find a frequency above 1 kHz at which output voltage is reduced by the same amount. Record this frequency as f_2. Note that during both these readings, the output of the signal generator should remain constant at its original value of amplitude. Check the output amplitude at both frequencies, f_1 and f_2, if there is any doubt.

The factor of 0.71 which you applied above corresponds to a loss of gain of 3dB. The frequencies f_1 and f_2 are therefore called the *lower* and the *upper 3dB points* respectively, and the range of frequencies between them is called the **bandwidth** of the amplifier. For an audio amplifier, f_1 and f_2 are quoted, so that such an amplifier can be described as being (for example) "3dB down at 17 Hz and at 35 kHz".

In short, the term "bandwidth", as applied to a tuned amplifier, means the quantity f_2 — f_1. A tuned amplifier can therefore be described as having (again for example) "a bandwidth of 10 kHz centred on f_r at 470 kHz".

The purpose of the 10nf capacitor C_4 connected across the load resistor R_3, is to ensure that the response of the amplifier at high frequencies will not be too wide.

Exercise 4.4
Still using the circuit of Fig. 4.13, observe the changing output waveform while signal generator output at 1 kHz is increased to 300 mV. Sketch the waveform which shows the distortion caused by overloading.

Next, restore the input to its previous value and connect an 8k2 resistor across R_1. Sketch the resulting output waveform, which will show the distortion caused by over-biasing.

With the resistor across R_1 removed, connect a 680-ohm resistor across R_2. Sketch the output waveform, which now shows the distortion caused by under-biasing.

The forms of distortion caused by overloading or by faulty biasing will be obvious when the output waveforms are viewed. Note, however, that smaller amounts of distortion caused by curvature of the characteristics are not visible on an output trace, and can only be detected by *distortion meters*. These filter out the sine-wave which is being amplified, leaving an output which consists only of the distortion, which can then be measured.

The Table below lists faults which have predictable effects, especially on gain and bandwidth.

FAULT	*EFFECTS*
Emitter Bypass Capacitor o/c	Reduced gain; Increased bandwidth.
Collector Load Resistance Too Low	Low gain; Collector voltage abnormally high.
Transistor Under-biased	Gain reduced; Some Signal Distortion at output.

Exercise 4.5
Construct the junction FET amplifier circuit shown in Fig. 4.14. The variable resistor R_2 should be set so that drain voltage is about 7V when there is no signal output.

Using the methods indicated in *Exercise 4.3*, find the gain at 1 kHz, the frequencies which produce the -3dB points, and note the distortion caused by overloading.

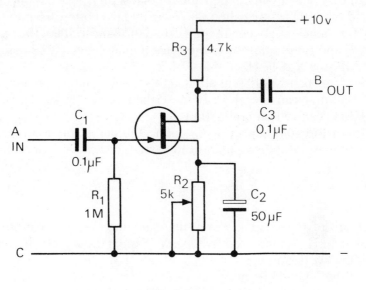

Fig. 4.14

SUMMARY

$$\text{Voltage Gain} = \frac{\text{Signal Voltage Out}}{\text{Signal Voltage In}}$$

In decibels, this becomes

$$\text{Voltage Gain} = 20 \log \frac{\text{Signal Voltage Out}}{\text{Signal Voltage In}}$$

The graph of voltage gain in decibels plotted against frequency shows the -3dB points at which the bandwidth of the amplifier is measured.

The bandwidth is taken as the useful operating frequency range of the amplifier.

Multiple-Stage Amplification

In many applications, a single transistor is not enough to provide sufficient gain, and several stages of amplification are needed. When an amplifier contains several stages, its total gain is given by the equation:—

$$G = G_1 \times G_2 \times G_3$$

where G_1, G_2, G_3 are the gains of the individual stages.

In decibels, this becomes

$$(\text{dB})_1 + (\text{dB})_2 + (\text{dB})_3$$

the total gain in decibels. Note that the decibel figures of gain are *added,* whereas the voltage (or current, or power) figures have to be *multiplied.* This is because logarithms are used in the construction of the decibel figure, and logarithmic addition is the equivalent of the multiplication of ordinary figures.

The coupling together of separate amplifying stages involves transferring the output signal from one stage to the input of the next stage. This can be done in several ways, as described below and illustrated in Fig. 4.15 (from which details of all biasing arrangements have been omitted for the sake of clarity):—

(a) *Direct coupling* involves connecting the output of one transistor to the input of the next, using only resistors or other components which will pass d.c. The result is that both d.c. and a.c. signals will be coupled. A d.c.-coupled amplifier by definition amplifies d.c. signals, so that a small change in the steady base voltage of the first stage will cause a large change in the steady collector voltage of the next. In all d.c.-coupled stages, particular attention needs to be paid to bias. A negative feedback biasing system is usually required.

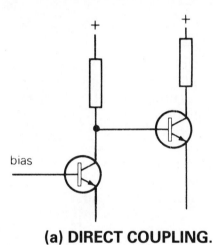

(a) DIRECT COUPLING.　　　　**(b) CAPACITOR-COUPLING.**

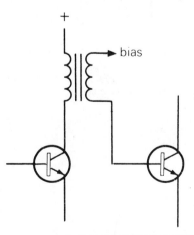

**(c) TRANSFORMER-
    COUPLING.**

Fig. 4.15

(b) *Capacitor-coupling* makes use of a capacitor placed in series between the output terminal of one stage and the input terminal of the next. The effect is that a.c. signals only can be coupled in this way, because d.c. levels cannot be transmitted through a capacitor. When amplifiers need a low -3dB point when input frequency is only a few Hz, large values of capacitance will be required.

(c) *Transformer-coupling* makes use of current signals flowing in the primary winding of a transformer connected into the collector circuit of a transistor to induce voltage signals in the secondary winding, which in turn is connected to the base of the next transistor. Once again, only a.c. signals can be so coupled; and a well-designed transformer will be needed if signals of only a few Hz are to be coupled. Note that the gain/frequency graph of a transformer-coupled amplifier can show unexpected peaks or dips caused by resonances.

The Use of Negative Feedback

Though it is possible to design single amplifier stages with fairly exact values of voltage gain (it is, for example, quite possible to design an amplifier with a voltage gain of exactly 29 times, if that should happen to be wanted), it is less easy to design multi-stage amplifiers that will give the precise voltage gain required. The reason is that the input and output resistances of transistors vary considerably, depending on the varying h_{fe} values of individual transistors, and that in any form of signal coupling the output resistance of one transistor forms a voltage divider with the input resistance of the next — so attenuating the signal. The point is simply illustrated in Fig. 4.16, in which R_1 symbolizes the output resistance of the first transistor and R_2 the input resistance of the second.

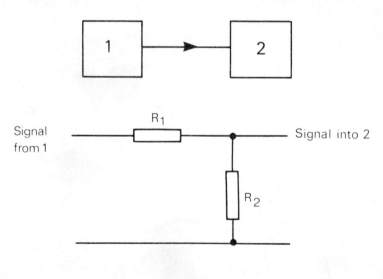

Fig. 4.16

A more promising way of designing an amplifier for a specified figure of gain is to aim for one which has too large a value of voltage gain, and then to use negative feedback to reduce this gain to the required figure. One advantage of using negative feedback is that it is often possible to calculate the gain of the complete amplifier without knowing any of the individual transistor gains or resistances. Very often the gain of the amplifier is simply the ratio of two values of fixed resistors.

For negative feedback to be useful, the gain of the amplifier without feedback (called the *open-loop gain*) must be much greater (100 times or more) than the gain of the

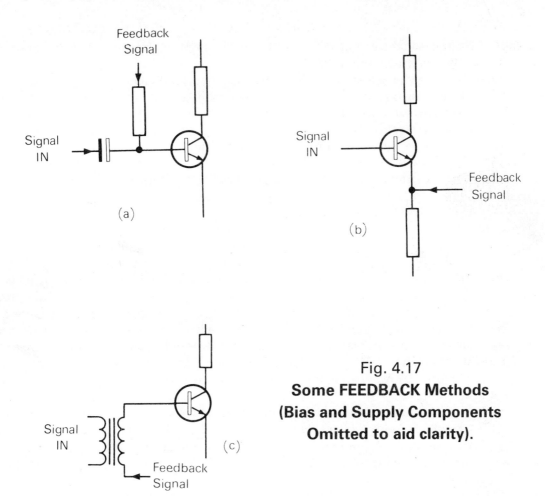

Fig. 4.17

Some FEEDBACK Methods (Bias and Supply Components Omitted to aid clarity).

(a) Shunt Feedback into the Base. (b) Series Feedback into the Emitter.
(c) Series Feedback using a Transformer.

amplifier when feedback is applied (the so-called *closed-loop gain*). When this situation exists, the factor $\dfrac{\text{Closed-Loop Gain}}{\text{Open-Loop Gain}}$ becomes important, because distortion and noise generated in the transistors or other components within the amplifier will be reduced by exactly the same ratio. If, for example, open-loop gain is 10 000, and closed-loop gain 100, then the factor $\dfrac{\text{Closed-Loop Gain}}{\text{Open-Loop Gain}}$ becomes $\dfrac{100}{10\ 000}$, or $\dfrac{1}{100}$ which means that the distortion will be reduced to 1/100th of its value in the open-loop amplifier.

Bandwidth, on the other hand, will be increased by the factor $\dfrac{\text{Open-Loop Gain}}{\text{Closed-Loop Gain}}$ (which is 100 times in the example above), on the assumption that no outside factor exists to limit bandwidth in any other way.

There are four principal ways in which negative feedback can be applied to an amplifier, depending on where the signal is taken from and to what point it is fed back.

(i) A signal fed back from a collector is called *voltage-derived*, because it is a sample of the output voltage signal.

(ii) A signal fed back from a resistor in the emitter circuit is called *current-derived*, because it is proportional to the output current signal and in the same phase as it.

(iii) A signal fed back to a base input is called a *shunt feedback signal*, because the feedback signal is in shunt (or parallel) with the normal input signal.

(iv) A signal fed back to the emitter of an input transistor is called a *series feedback signal*, because the feedback signal is in series with the normal input signal. An alternative method of achieving a series feedback signal is to transformer-couple the feedback to the base of a transistor through the transformer winding, as shown in Fig. 4.17(c).

Each of these methods of applying negative feedback will have the desired effects of reducing gain, noise and distortion, and of increasing bandwidth; but the different methods of connection can affect other features of the complete amplifier. Taking the feedback from the emitter of an output stage, for example, causes the output resistance at the collector of the same transistor to be higher than it would be if the feedback were to be taken from the collector. Alternatively, taking the feedback to a base input causes the input resistance to be lower (often much lower) than it would be if the feedback were to be taken to the emitter.

Some feedback circuits include the input or output resistance of the transistor itself as part of the feedback loop, and are therefore less predictable in action.

Fig. 4.18 shows two common types of feedback circuit. Fig. 4.18(a) uses negative feedback from the emitter of Tr2 to the base of Tr1. The feedback is therefore series-derived and shunt-fed.

Fig. 4.18(b) shows negative feedback from the collector of Tr2 to the emitter of Tr1. The feedback is therefore shunt-derived and series-fed.

The Table below shows the effect of some component failures on both these circuits.

Fault	*Effects*
R_9 or C_5 o/c	No Negative Feedback, High Gain but Possible Instability.
s/c across R_9	Greatly Reduced Gain.
C_5 s/c	Bias of Tr1 Incorrect.

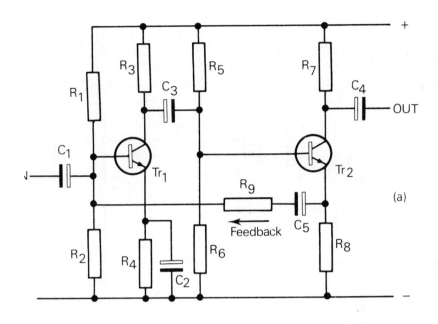

(a)

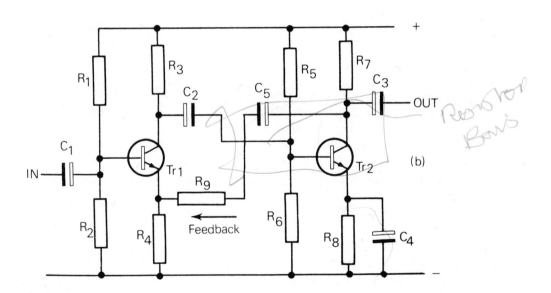

(b)

Fig. 4.18   **Two Common Types of Feedback Circuit.**

Exercise 4.6
Construct the circuit shown in Fig. 4.19. Both Tr1 and Tr2 can be any general-purpose silicon NPN transistor. Then observe the effects of two different types of feedback.

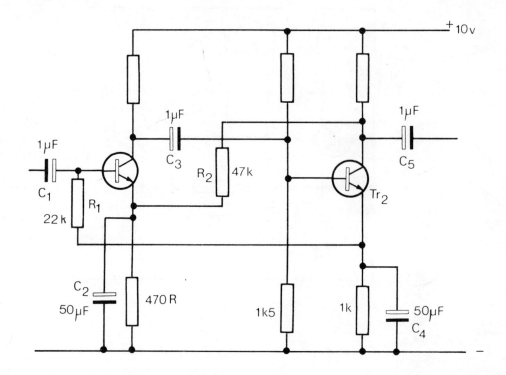

Fig. 4.19

(a) *Series-derived, shunt-fed.* Measure the voltage gain of the complete amplifier. (Note that a small input signal should be used to prevent overloading). Now remove C_4, so introducing negative feedback through R_1. Measure and note the new value of voltage gain.

(b) *Shunt-derived, series-fed.* Replace C_4, remove C_2, and again measure the value of circuit gain. This gain is now the loop gain of the feedback loop through R_2. Note its value, and compare with (a) above.

SUMMARY
If more gain is required than can be achieved by a single-stage transistor amplifier, several stages of amplification can be coupled together.

Coupling can either be direct, or achieved by means of capacitors or transformers.

The value of gain can be fixed precisely by using negative feedback. Negative feedback reduces gain, but also reduces the effect of component variations on that gain. Correctly applied, negative feedback also reduces distortion and noise, and widens bandwidth.

CHAPTER 5
Power Amplifiers and Power Supply Units

Both voltage amplifiers and current amplifiers play important parts in electronic circuits, but not all of them are capable of supplying some types of load. For instance, a voltage amplifier with a gain of 100 times may be well able to feed a 10V signal into a 10k load resistance, but quite incapable of feeding even a 1V signal into a 10-ohm load. A current amplifier with a gain of 1 000 may be excellent for amplifying a 1μA signal into a 1 mA signal, but cannot convert a 1 mA signal at 10V into a 1A signal at the same voltage.

The missing factor common to both these examples is **power**. A signal of 1A (r.m.s.) at 10V (r.m.s.) represents a power output of 10W, and the small transistors which are used for voltage or current amplification cannot handle such levels of power without overheating.

Transistors intended to pass large currents at voltage levels of more than a volt or so must have the following characteristics:

(1) They must have low output resistance; and
(2) They must have good ability to dissipate heat.

A low output resistance is necessary because a transistor with a high output resistance will dissipate too much power when large currents flow through it. Low resistance is achieved by making the area of the junctions much larger than is normal for a small-signal transistor.

The ability to dissipate heat is necessary in order that the electrical energy which is converted into heat in the transistor can be easily removed. If it were not, the temperature of the transistor (notably its collector-base junction) would keep rising until the junctions were permanently destroyed.

Given suitable transistors with large junction areas and good heat conductivity to the metal case, the problem of power amplification becomes one of using suitable circuits and of dissipating the heat from the transistor.

Heat Sinks

Heat sinks take the form of finned metal clips, blocks or sheets which act as convectors passing heat from the body of a transistor into the air. Good contact between the body of the transistor and the heat sink is essential, and *silicone grease* (also called *heat-sink grease*) is useful in promoting this contact.

Many types of power transistor have their metal cases connected to the collector terminal. It is therefore necessary to insulate them from their heat sinks. This is done by using thin mica washers between transistor and heat sink, with insulating bushes inserted

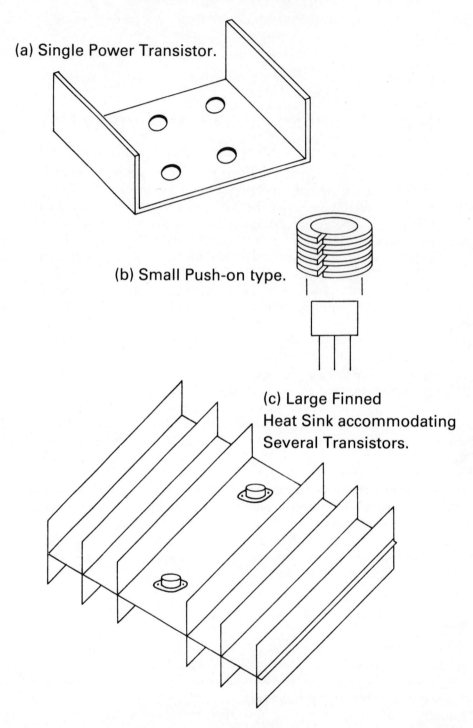

(a) Single Power Transistor.

(b) Small Push-on type.

(c) Large Finned
Heat Sink accommodating
Several Transistors.

Fig. 5.1   **HEAT SINKS.**

on the fixing-bolts in addition. Heat-sink grease should always be smeared on both sides of all such washers.

Class A and Class B

Several different methods exist for biasing transistors which are to be used in power output stages. "Class A" and "Class B" are names given to two types of commonly-used biasing systems.

In a Class A stage, the transistor is so biased that the collector voltage is never bottomed, nor is current flow cut off. Output current flows for the whole of the input cycle. It is the same bias system, in fact, as is used in linear voltage amplifiers.

Class A operation of a transistor ensures good linearity, but suffers from two disadvantages:—

(a) A large current flows through the transistor at all times, so that the transistor needs to dissipate a considerable amount of power.

(b) This loss of power in the transistor inevitably means that less power is available for dissipation in the load, and a Class A stage can never be more than about 30% efficient.

Even in an ideal Class A amplifier, with the load and amplifier output resistances matched, only some 50% of the available power would be delivered to the load, with the remaining 50% being dissipated by the amplifier in the form of heat. When the resistances are mismatched, the power transfer ratio is even lower.

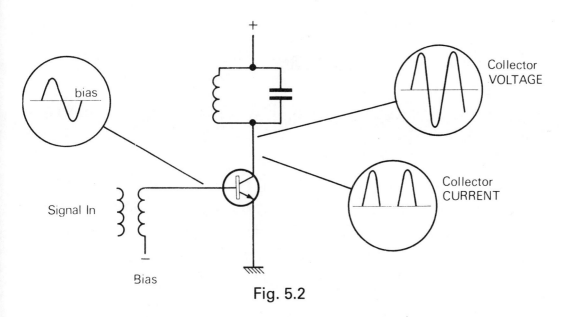

Fig. 5.2

A CLASS B RADIO-FREQUENCY AMPLIFIER.

Though the transistor conducts for only half the duration of the input wave, the tuned circuit restores the remainder of the sine-wave.

In a Class B amplifier, the power transistor conducts for only one-half of the duration of the input sine-wave. A single transistor is therefore unusable unless the other half of the wave can be obtained in some other way.

At radio frequencies this can be done by making use of a load which is a resonant circuit (a so-called *tank circuit*). The tank circuit is made to oscillate by the conduction of the transistor, and the action of the resonant circuit continues the oscillation during the period when the transistor is cut off.

This principle can only be applied, however, if the signal to be amplified is of fairly high frequency. This is because the values of inductance and capacitance needed to produce resonance at, say, audio frequencies would be too large to be practical; and because a load of such a size would in any case too greatly restrict the bandwidth.

An alternative method which is used at audio and other low frequencies is to use two transistors, each conducting on different halves of the input wave. Such an arrangement is called a *push-pull* circuit. Push-pull circuits can be used in Class A amplification, but are essential for use in Class B.

Class B stages possess the following advantages over Class A:—

1. Very little steady bias current flows in them, so that the amplifier has only a negligible amount of power to dissipate when no signal is applied.

2. Their theoretical maximum efficiency is 78.4%, and practical amplifiers can achieve efficiencies of between 50% and 60%. This means that more power is dissipated in the load itself, and less wasted as heat by the transistors.

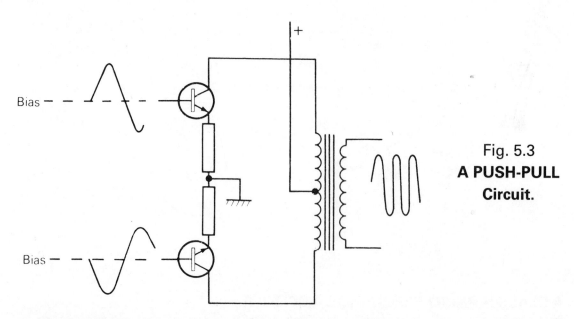

Fig. 5.3
**A PUSH-PULL
Circuit.**

Both transistors feed current through the transformer, but in opposite directions. The transformer then combines the two outputs.

The disadvantages of Class B compared to Class A are that:—

1. The supply current changes as the signal amplitude changes, so that a stabilised supply (see below) is often needed.

2. More signal distortion is caused, especially at that part of the signal where one transistor cuts off and the other starts to conduct. This part of the signal is called the *cross-over region*.

Typical Class A and Class B Circuits
Fig. 5.4 illustrates a single-transistor amplifier biased in Class A. Because no d.c. can be allowed to flow in the load (which is in this case a loudspeaker), a transformer is used to couple the signal from the transistor to the load.

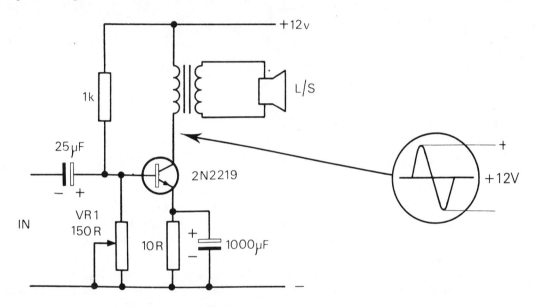

Fig. 5.4   **A single-transistor CLASS A AMPLIFIER.**

With no signal input, the steady current through the transistor is about 50mA and the supply voltage is 12V. Because of the low resistance of the primary winding of the transformer, the voltage at the collector of the transistor is about equal to the supply voltage.

When a signal is applied, the collector voltage swings below supply voltage on one peak of the signal and the same distance above the supply voltage on the other peak of the signal. By reason of this transformer action, therefore, the *average* voltage at the collector of the transistor remains at supply voltage when a signal is present.

It follows that in a Class A stage of this type, the current taken from the supply is constant whether a signal is amplified or not. Any variation in current flow from no-signal to full-signal conditions indicates that some non-linearity, and therefore distortion, must be present.

A circuit often used for Class B amplifiers is shown in Fig. 5.5. It is known as the *single-ended push-pull* or *totem-pole* circuit.

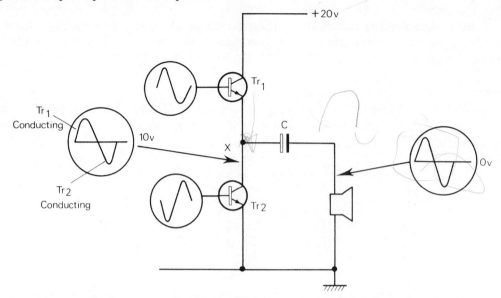

Fig. 5.5   **A single-ended PUSH-PULL, or "TOTEM-POLE" circuit.**

Two power transistors are connected in series, with their mid-connection (Point X in the Fig.) coupled through a capacitor to the load — which may be either a loudspeaker, the field coils of a TV receiver, or the armature of a servomotor. During the positive half of the signal cycle Tr1 conducts, so that the output signal drives current through the load from X to ground. During the negative half of the cycle, Tr1 is cut off and Tr2 conducts, so that the current now flows in the opposite direction, through the load and Tr2.

The coupling capacitor C_2 forms an essential part of the circuit. When there is no signal input, C_2 is charged to about half supply voltage (*i.e.*, the voltage at Point X). The voltage swing at this Point X, from full supply voltage in one direction to ground or zero voltage in the other, thus becomes at the load a voltage swing of identical amplitude centred round zero volts.

SUMMARY
Transistor power amplifiers require transistors possessing low resistance and good ability to dissipate heat. In particular, the output transistor(s) must be tightly connected to a heat sink.

Class A stages, which pass large standing currents of steady value, need larger heat sinks than do Class B stages, which dissipate much less power in the transistors when no signal is applied.

Bias and Feedback

Class A output stages need a bias system which will keep almost constant the standing current (*i.e*, the d.c. current with no signal input) flowing through them, despite the large temperature changes to which the standing current itself gives rise. One common method, illustrated in Fig. 5.6, is to use a silicon diode as part of the bias network. The diode should be a junction diode attached to the same heat sink as the power transistor(s).

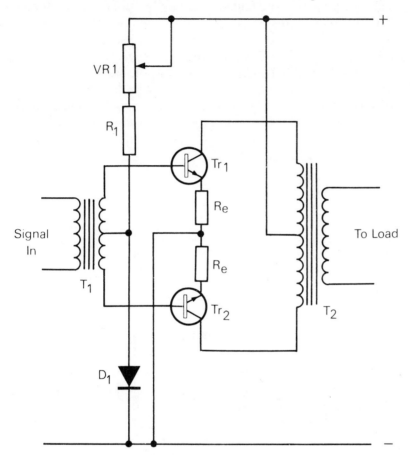

Fig. 5.6   A Silicon Diode connected for use as BIAS CONTROL.

As a silicon junction is heated, the junction voltage (about 0.6V at low temperatures) which is needed for correct bias becomes less. A fixed-voltage bias supply composed of resistors would therefore over-bias the transistor as the temperature increased. A silicon diode compensates for the change in the base-emitter voltage of the transistor, since the forward voltage of the diode is also reduced as its temperature rises.

The Class A push-pull stage in Fig. 5.6 uses two silicon transistors coupled to the load by a transformer. The input signal also is coupled to the stage by a transformer, which ensures that both transistors obtain the correct phase of signal.

The bias current for this circuit is taken to the centre-tap of the secondary winding of the phase-splitter (or *driver*) transformer T_1, and some additional stability is obtained by using the negative feedback resistors R_e in the emitter leads. Any increase in the bias current of the power transistors will cause the emitter voltage of both transistors to rise, so reducing the voltage between base and emitter and thereby giving back-bias to the input.

In both the circuits described in Fig. 5.4 and 5.6 the bias is adjusted so that the correct amount of steady bias current flows in the output stage. To adjust this bias current in the single-transistor stage requires that the collector circuit be broken to connect in a current meter, and that VR_1 be then adjusted so as to give the correct current reading. The push-pull circuit (Fig. 5.6) can be set by measuring the voltage across the emitter resistors, R_e, and by adjusting VR_1 to give the correct value of voltage at these points.

A more elaborate circuit using the Class AB totem-pole stage is shown in Fig. 5.7. In Class AB, each amplifier is biased to a value lying between those appropriate for either Class A or Class B. The output current in each stage thus flows for slightly more than half of each input cycle. The effect is to minimise cross-over distortion.

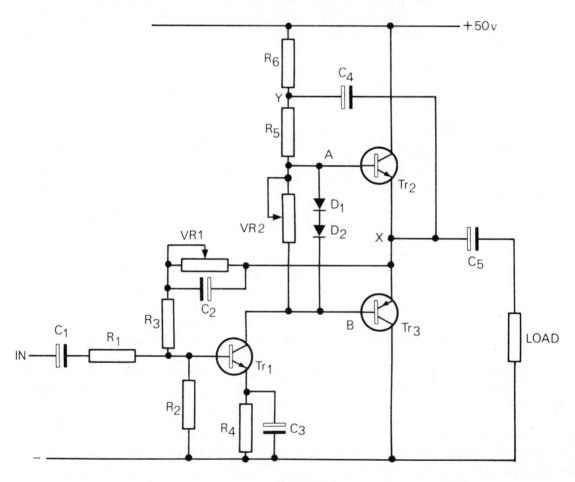

Fig. 5.7

A Complementary Output Stage of the Totem-Pole type,
with Driving Stage and Feedback Connections.

In this circuit, both a.c. and d.c. feedback loops are used. The d.c. feedback is used to keep the steady bias current at its correct low value, and the a.c. feedback is used to correct the distortions caused by Class B operation — in particular the cross-over distortion.

Two bias-adjusting settings are needed in this circuit. The potentiometer VR_1 sets the value of the bias current in Tr1, so that the amount of current flowing through resistors R_2, R_3 and VR_2 is controlled. The potentiometer is adjusted so that the voltage at Point X is exactly half the supply voltage when there is no signal input. Potentiometer VR_2 controls the amount of current passing through the output transistors.

This type of output circuit is called a *complementary* stage, because it uses complementary transistors, one NPN and one PNP type, both connected as emitter followers. With the emitters of both Tr2 and Tr3 connected to the voltage at Point X, both output transistors are almost cut off when no signal is present. When VR_2 is correctly adjusted, the voltage drop between Points A and B is just enough to give the output transistors a small standing bias current (2 to 20 mA) to ensure that they never cut off together. The value of this steady current is usually set low so as to keep cross-over distortion to a minimum — with the actual value that recommended by the manufacturers.

A current meter must be used to check the value of bias current.

It will be seen that there are two a.c. feedback loops in this Fig. 5.7 amplifier. Negative feedback, to improve linearity, is taken through C_2, and positive feedback is taken through C_4 to Point Y. This positive feedback, sometimes called *boot-strapping*, cannot cause oscillation because the feedback signal is of smaller amplitude than is the normal input signal at that point (an emitter follower has a voltage gain slightly lower than unity). It has, however, the desirable effect of decreasing the amount of signal amplitude needed at the input to Tr2.

Impedance Matching

The ideal method of delivering power to a load would be to use transistors which had a very low resistance, so that most of the power (I^2R) was dissipated in the load. Most audio amplifiers today make use of such transistors to drive 8-ohm loudspeaker loads.

For some purposes, however, transistors offering higher resistance must be used or loads possessing very low resistance must be driven, and a transformer must therefore be used to match the differing impedances. In public address systems, for example, where loudspeakers are situated at considerable distances from the amplifier, it is normal to use high-voltage signals (100V) at low currents so as to avoid I^2R losses in the lines. In such cases the 8-ohm loudspeakers must be coupled to the lines through transformers.

The transformer ratio giving the best transfer of power is expressed by the formula:

$$N = \sqrt{\frac{\text{Output Impedance of Amplifier}}{\text{Impedance of Load}}}$$

where N is the ratio of the number of turns in the primary winding of the transformer to the number of turns in the secondary winding.

Example. A power amplifier stage operates with a 64-ohm output impedance. What transformer ratio is needed for maximum power transfer to an 8-ohm load?

Solution. $N = \sqrt{\dfrac{64}{8}} = \sqrt{8} = 2.8$. A 3:1 step-down transformer would therefore be used.

Exercise 5.1

Set up the circuit shown in Fig. 5.8, using a multi-ratio output transformer. TR1 can be either a 2N3053 or a BFY50, TR2 a 2N3055 and D1 a 1N4001.

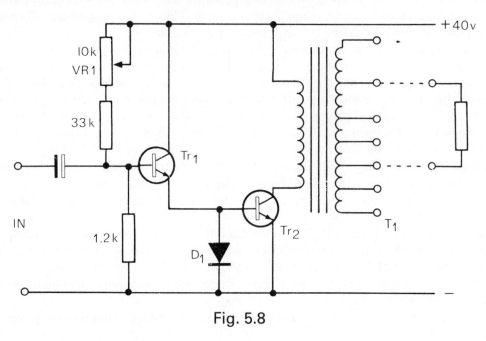

Fig. 5.8

With a 40V supply, adjust VR_1 so that the standing d.c. current flow through Tr2 is 50 mA. Connect the 8-ohm resistor between two of the taps of the secondary of the transformer and connect the signal generator to the input. Connect an oscilloscope across the 8-ohm resistor.

Applying a 400 Hz signal, adjust input signal voltage so that a 2V peak-to-peak signal is observed across the 8-ohm resistor. Now, without altering the signal generator settings, switch off the amplifier, change the transformer connections so as to alter the ratio, and switch on again. Measure the output voltage.

Repeat the procedure so that the output voltage is measured for every possible pair of secondary tapping points. What transformer ratio gives the maximum signal output? Is the setting critical?

Exercise 5.2

Connect into the power amplifier of *Exercise 5.1* (or any other suitable amplifier), an 8-ohm load resistor, and adjust the signal generator to give a 2V peak-to-peak output across it. Vary the frequency of the signal generator, first down to the frequency at which the voltage output is 1.4V (0.707 × 2V), or "3 dB down", and then upwards to the frequency at which the output is again 1.4V, or "3 dB up". Note these 3 dB frequencies.

It will be seen that at each of these "3 dB" frequencies the power output of the amplifier is half as much as it is at 400 Hz ($0.707 \times 0.707 \simeq 0.5$). The frequencies are therefore known as the *half-power points*. Note the power bandwidth of the amplifier, which is the frequency range between the half-power points.

SUMMARY

Bias systems for power output stages must keep the bias current steady over a wide range of temperatures. This is more difficult in Class A stages, because they operate with large bias currents.

Signal coupling from amplifier to load is generally by capacitor or transformer, but sometimes direct.

When a transformer is used to couple stages of unequal resistance, the transformer ratio must be chosen so as to match correctly the impedances of the two stages.

Faults

Faults in output stages are usually caused by over-dissipation of power, which in turn can be caused by over-loading or over-heating. An output stage can be over-loaded, when capacitor coupling is used, by connecting a load having too low a resistance. The usual result is to burn out the output transistor(s).

In most Class AB totem-pole circuits, even the most momentary short circuit at the output (caused for example, by faulty connections) will cause the output transistor (usually Tr2 in Fig. 5.7) to burn out if a signal is being amplified.

Excessive bias currents can often be traced to the failure of a diode in the bias chain, or to a burn-out of the biasing potentiometer in a totem-pole circuit.

Unexpected clipping of the output can be caused by failure of the bootstrap capacitor (C_4 in Fig. 5.7), or by a fault in the bias resistors which has caused the voltage at Point X to drift up or down.

Power Supplies — Regulation

The simplest possible power-supply circuits consist of rectifiers and smoothing capacitors, which have already been covered in Chapter 2. In these circuits, the reservoir capacitor supplies the current to the load during the time when the diodes are cut off, and any ripple on the supply is reduced by filtering. Such circuits are adequate for many purposes, but they are too poorly regulated for use in circuits intended for measurement, computing, broadcasting or process control.

The *regulation* of a circuit is the term used to express the change of output voltage caused either by a change in the a.c. supply voltage or by a change in the output load current. A well-regulated supply will have an output voltage whose value is almost constant; the output voltage of a poorly-regulated supply will change considerably when either the a.c. input voltage or the output current changes. The Table on page 28 shows how the voltage of a smoothed supply changes from no-load to maximum-load condition.

The change in output voltage caused by changes in the a.c. supply voltage is usually less great. A 10% change in the a.c. supply will also change the output voltage of a simple

power supply by about 10% — the two percentage changes being almost identical.
Example. What will be the change in a 10V supply when the a.c. supply voltage changes
from 240V to 220V?
Solution. The a.c. voltage change is 20V down on 240. The percentage change is therefore
$\frac{20}{240} \times 100 = 8.3\%$. Since 8.3% of 10V is 0.83V, the 10V supply will drop to $10 - 0.83V$

$= 9.17V$.

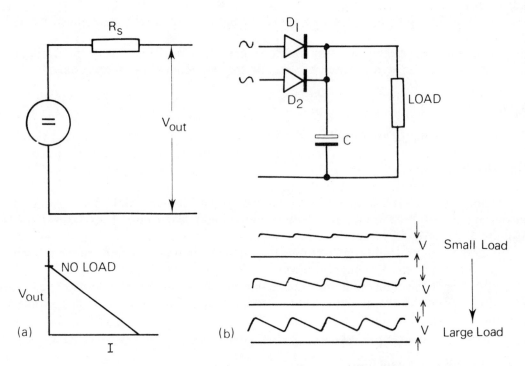

Fig. 5.9   **THE CAUSES OF POOR REGULATION.**

**(a) The Combined Resistances of Circuit Rectifiers, Transformer Windings,
      etc.**

(b) The Charge and Discharge of the Reservoir Capacitor.

The effect of changes in the load current (which are themselves caused by changes in
the load resistance) is more complicated, because there are two such effects. The first is
brought about by the resistances of the rectifiers, the transformer windings and any
inductors which may be used in filter circuits, and by the internal resistance of the power
supply. By Ohm's law, a change of current flow through such resistances *must* cause a
change of voltage.

The second effect lies in the voltage drop which takes place across the reservoir capacitor as more current is drawn from it. This voltage drop (V) can be quantified by the equation:

$$V = \frac{I \times t}{C}$$

where I is the load current in amps, *t* the time in seconds elapsing between one charge from the reservoir and the next, and *C* the capacitance in farads of the reservoir.

Example. By how much will the voltage across a 220µF capacitor drop when 0.2A is drawn from a full-wave rectifying circuit?

Solution. In a full-wave rectifying circuit, the time between peaks is 10 ms.

Substituting the data in the equation $V = \frac{I \times t}{C}$,

$$V = \frac{0.2 \times 0.01}{220 \times 10^{-6}} = 9V$$

A 50V supply, for example, would give an output which drops to 41V between peaks, and a 9V ripple at 100 Hz would be present.

SUMMARY

The simple rectifier-reservoir power supply gives poor regulation. Its output voltage is proportional to the a.c. input voltage; and the effect of the load current on the circuit resistances and on the charge on the reservoir capacitor causes sharp voltage drops and a large amount of ripple at maximum d.c. current flow.

Regulator Circuits

A regulator circuit connected to a rectifier/reservoir unit ensures that the output voltage is steady for all designed values of load current or of a.c. supply voltage. Such a circuit can only do its job, however, if the rectifier/reservoir unit itself is capable of supplying the required output voltage (measured from the minimum of the ripple wave) under the worst possible conditions, *i.e.*, when a.c. supply voltage is minimum and load current is maximum. The regulator will then prevent the output voltage from rising above this set value even when load current is small or the a.c. supply voltage high.

Two types of regulator are used — a series circuit and a shunt circuit. The simplest example of the shunt type is a Zener diode regulator shown in Fig. 5.10. In this type of circuit, the amount of current drawn from the power supply is constant. When load current is maximum, the regulator circuit current is minimum. When the load takes its minimum current, the regulator circuit takes its maximum current. The arrangement is therefore such that load current plus regulator current is always a constant value. The constant current flowing through R produces a constant voltage drop across it. So if the input voltage remains unchanged, the output voltage will remain constant also.

If the supply voltage changes, the total current will change to a new value, but the action of the Zener diode ensures that there is no change in output voltage.

Some care has to be taken, however, over the power ratings of the Zener diode and of its supply resistor. The maximum dissipation of the Zener diode in the circuit is:— Zener

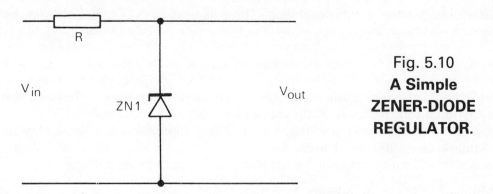

Fig. 5.10
**A Simple
ZENER-DIODE
REGULATOR.**

Voltage × Maximum Current — with dissipation in milliwatts if the current is measured in mA.

The maximum dissipation of the resistor is given by:—

(Unregulated Voltage — Zener Voltage) × Maximum Current.

Example. A 5.6V Zener diode is used to supply a load which takes a maximum current of 15 mA. If the minimum desirable Zener current is 2 mA, and the unregulated voltage is 12V, find *(a)* the value of series resistance which must be used, *(b)* the maximum Zener dissipation and *(c)* the maximum dissipation in the resistor.

Solution. With 15 mA flowing through the load and 2 mA through the Zener diode, total current is 17 mA. The voltage across the resistor is (12 − 5.6 =) 6.4V, so that *(a)* the required resistance value, using Ohm's law, is $\frac{6.4}{17}$ = 0.376k or 376 ohms. In practice a 330-ohm resistor would be used, making the total current $\frac{6.4}{.330}$ mA = 19.4 mA.

(b) At a current of 19.4 mA, the dissipation in the Zener diode is 5.6 × 19.4 = 108.6 mW; and *(c)* the dissipation in the resistor is 6.4 × 19.4 = 124.2 mW.

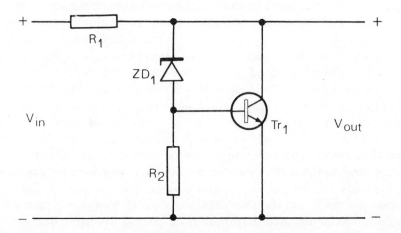

Fig. 5.11   **The "AMPLIFIED-ZENER" REGULATOR Circuit.**

When the circuit requires that much larger currents than about 20 mA be passed through the stabiliser, the circuit shown in Fig. 5.11 can be used. In this circuit, the Zener diode supplies the base current for a power transistor connected as a shunt regulator.

For the transistor to conduct, its base voltage must be about 0.6V higher than its emitter voltage, so that the voltage at its collector must be about Zener voltage +0.6V. Any rise in the collector voltage would cause an equal rise of voltage at the base, because the Zener diode keeps the voltage between base and collector constant. A larger base voltage would cause a much higher collector current (remember that a rise of 60 mV in base voltage causes collector current flow to increase by ten times), and the voltage drop across the series resistor would thus restore the correct operating conditions.

This negative feedback arrangement is sometimes called an *amplified Zener circuit*.

Both the straightforward Zener diode and the amplified Zener circuits have the additional advantage that they greatly reduce the amount of hum ripple from the power supply, provided that the amount of current being taken from the supply does not cause the minimum voltage to drop below the regulated output voltage.

The output voltage will not change noticeably when the a.c. supply voltage changes, provided that the voltage does not fall below the level needed to keep current flowing through the Zener diode.

Exercise 5.3
Using a simple rectifier-plus-reservoir power supply, plot regulation curves. Supply the a.c. input through a Variac auto-transformer, and read off the input a.c. voltage with an a.c. voltmeter — *making sure that all connections are insulated before switching on.*

Now use a d.c. voltmeter to measure the output voltage of the power supply. With no

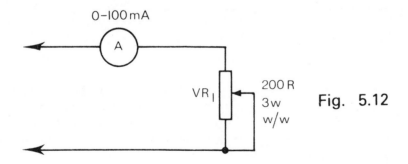

Fig. 5.12

load, measure output voltage for a.c. input voltages ranging from 90% to 110% of normal line voltage, entering your results on a graph of output voltage plotted against input (a.c.) voltage.

Now set the input a.c. voltage to normal line voltage, and add the load and ammeter circuit of Fig. 5.12. Note the value of output voltage for currents of 0, 10 mA, 50 mA, 75 mA and 100 mA, and plot a graph of output voltage against load current.

These two graphs form the regulation graphs for the power supply.

Exercise 5.4
Make up the regulator circuit shown in Fig. 5.11 with the following values of component:— R_1 — 33R, 1W (W/W — or Wire-Wound); ZD_1 — 5.6V; R_2 — 330R; Tr1 — 2N3055; V_{in} — 10V. Connect this circuit to the power supply used in *Exercise 5.3*, and draw another set of regulation curves for the regulated output. Measure also the ripple at 100 mA load current *(a)* across the reservoir capacitor and *(b)* across the load.

The other way of regulating the output of a power supply is by means of a series regulator in which a transistor is connected between the supply and the load, as indicated in Fig. 5.13.

When this type of regulator circuit is used, the transistor takes only as much current as the load — unlike the shunt regulator which takes its maximum current just as the load takes minimum current. The base voltage of Tr1 is held constant by the regulator action of ZD1 and R1. The emitter voltage, and so the conduction, of Tr1 depends on the load voltage. If the demand for load current increases, the output voltage will tend to fall, increasing the forward bias of Tr1. This allows it to pass more current to meet the demand.

If the requirement for load current falls, this effect will be reversed.

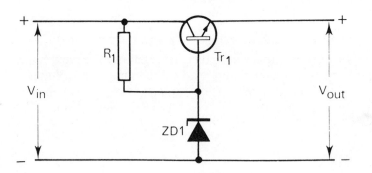

Fig. 5.13

The SERIES REGULATOR.

Exercise 5.5
Make up the simple series regulator circuit of Fig. 5.13 with the following component values:— R_1 — 330R; ZD_1 — 5.6V; Tr1 — 2N3055; V_{in} — 10V. Connect this circuit to the power supply previously used, and draw a set of regulation curves for the stabilised circuit.

Measure also the ripple voltage at maximum load current *(a)* across the reservoir capacitor and *(b)* across the load.

More elaborate series regulator circuits use comparator amplifiers to drive the series transistor.

In the circuit pictured in Fig. 5.14, the positive (in-phase) input to a comparator amplifier labelled OPA1 is connected to a Zener diode so that its voltage is fixed. The negative (anti-phase) input is connected to the output of the power supply through a potential divider. The output of the comparator drives the series transistor so that any drop in the output voltage is at once counteracted by the flow of more current through the transistor.

Excellent regulation can be provided by such a circuit, which is nowadays available complete in integrated form.

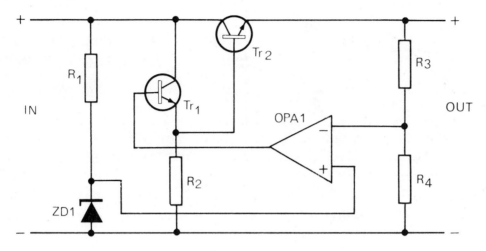

Fig. 5.14
A Series Regulator Circuit containing a Comparator Amplifier.

Fault-finding

Failure in regulator circuits is usually caused by excessive dissipation in the main transistor, be it shunt or series as the case may be.

In the series circuit the over-dissipation will have been caused by an excessive load current, unless the regulator is protected against short circuits.

In a shunt circuit, excessive load current will not directly damage the main transistor; but it will often impair the series resistor so that, when the load is removed, excessive current flow will then pass through the shunt transistor.

An o/c Zener diode will cause a shunt regulator to cease conducting. Its effect on the series circuit is the opposite, in that the output voltage will rise to the level of the unregulated supply.

A s/c Zener diode will cause the shunt circuit to pass excessive current. It will cause the series circuit to cut off.

Note carefully that all power transistors used in regulator circuits must be bolted to heat sinks of adequate size.

Voltage-Doubler Circuits

There are a few circuits which call for a high-voltage, low-current supply in which poor regulation is acceptable. Rather than wind a transformer especially to provide the high voltage, a *voltage multiplier* circuit (of which the *voltage doubler* is the simplest example) is often used instead.

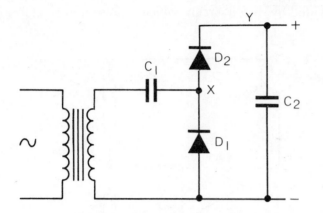

Fig. 5.15
A VOLTAGE-DOUBLER
Circuit.

On the negative-going half of the voltage cycle shown in Fig. 5.15, C_1 is charged by current through D_1, so that Point X is at a d.c. voltage equal to the peak voltage of the a.c. wave.

At the peak of the positive-going half-cycle, the peak inverse voltage across D_1 is equal to twice the peak voltage (the previous peak charge, plus the peak a.c. value). This causes C_2 to charge to the same level through D_2.

At line (supply) frequencies, the capacitor C_1 must be of large value, and must, of course, be rated at the full d.c. voltage. At higher frequencies, smaller values of capacitance can be used.

Multiplier circuits of this type are commonly used to supply the high voltages required by the colour tubes in colour TV receivers.

The circuit shown in Fig. 5.16(a) is effectively two voltage-doublers connected in series, while Fig. 5.16(b) shows the so-called *Cockcroft-Walton Multiplier*. Circuits such as these are commonly used to obtain voltages as high as 25kV for the final anode electrode of the tube.

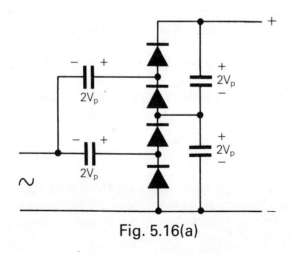

Fig. 5.16
The VOLTAGE-QUADRUPLER (a)
Circuit:
Alternative Configurations (b).

Fig. 5.16(a)

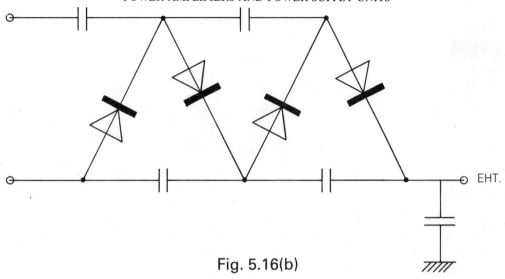

Fig. 5.16(b)

SUMMARY

Regulator circuits are used to keep steady the output voltage from a power supply, at a value equal to the lowest voltage output from the reservoir capacitor on full load and with minimum a.c. input voltage.

Either shunt or series regulators (sometimes also called *stabilisers*) can be used. Either type of circuit provides great improvement in regulation and control of ripple; but the series circuit is in more common use, apart from the simple Zener diode regulator.

In high-voltage supplies, the use of voltage-multiplier circuits provides an alternative to relatively expensive high-voltage transformer windings.

CHAPTER 6
LCR Circuits

D.C. Circuits

In any circuit receiving a steady d.c. supply voltage, a resistor will act to control current flow. The equation to determine the value of that flow is Ohm's law in its $I = V/R$ form. If there is neither inductance nor capacitance in the circuit, the value of current given by the Ohm's law equation will start to flow at the instant the voltage V is switched on, and will continue to flow for as long as that voltage continues to be applied. If the value of the voltage is changed, the value of the current will change also — but the strict relationship $I = V/R$ will always be preserved.

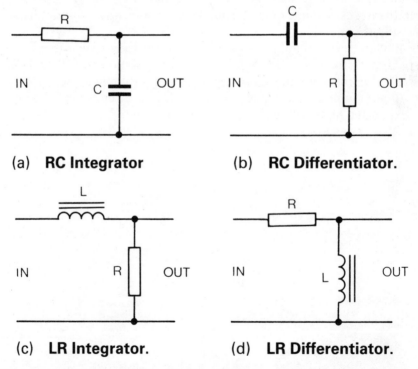

(a)   **RC Integrator**   (b)   **RC Differentiator.**

(c)   **LR Integrator.**   (d)   **LR Differentiator.**

Fig. 6.1

Some Circuits in which TRANSIENT CURRENTS can Flow.

The circuits shown in Fig 6.1, however, contain either capacitors or inductors as well as resistors. The addition of such components to a d.c. circuit causes the value of current flow in the circuit to vary for a short time after the circuit voltage is switched on, before finally settling down at the value which the use of Ohm's law would predict. It is important to distinguish between the *steady* current, which is the final value of current, and the *transient* current, which is the changing value flowing just after the circuit has been switched either on or off.

The time during which the transient current flows is important. It is measured by a quantity called the **time constant** of the circuit in question, and it can be calculated for every circuit in which the values of the various components are known. When a time equal to *four time constants* has elapsed after a circuit has been switched on, the transient current flows have dropped virtually to zero, and the steady current is flowing.

The Steady Current

The amount of steady current flowing in the circuit is obviously affected by the resistance of the circuit. Circuits in which a capacitor is connected in series will have zero steady current because a capacitor acts as an insulator, or open circuit, for d.c. Circuits in which an inductor is connected in series will have a steady value of d.c. current flow that depends on the value of the resistance R of the inductor.

Example. A 2H,1 500-ohm inductor has a 1k5 resistor connected in series with it, and is itself connected across a 10V d.c. supply. What steady value of current will eventually flow?

Solution. The total value of resistance is 3k, connected across 10V. The value of steady current flow, in mA, will therefore be $10/3 = 3.3$ mA. The two-henry inductance value of the coil is not relevant in this calculation.

Capacitors connected in parallel have no effect on the value of the steady current. Inductors connected in parallel act in the same way as resistors insofar as the steady current is concerned, and have the same effects.

Transient Currents

Both inductors and capacitors have a big influence on the transient currents that flow for the instants that elapse just after a d.c. circuit is switched on. The essential facts to remember are as follows:—

1. The *voltage across a capacitor* cannot change instantly, but only at a rate decided by the time constant of the circuit — i.e., its $C \times R$ — where C is the value of the capacitance in farads, and R is the value of the resistance in ohms.

2. The *amount of current flowing through an inductor* cannot change instantly, but only at a rate determined by the time constant of the circuit — i.e., L/R — where L is the value of the inductance in henries and R is the value of the resistance in ohms.

Exercise 6.1

Connect the circuit shown in Fig. 6.2(a). The inductor L should be of the high-inductance, low-resistance type. Set the stop-clock to zero, but be ready to start it the instant the circuit is switched on. (An electric clock is obviously ideal for the purpose).

Note the values of current flow against time elapsed for the first few seconds after switching on, and plot these values on a graph. The shape of the curve you will obtain is shown in Fig. 6.2(b).

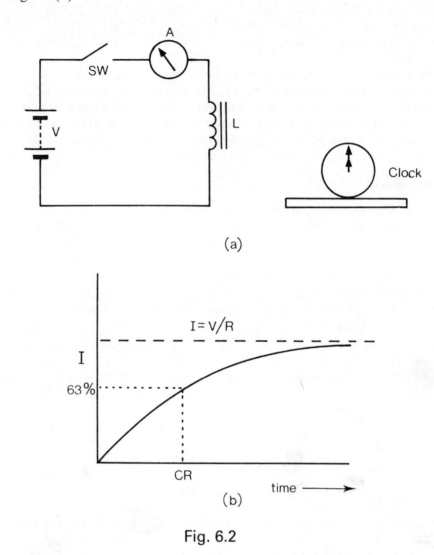

Fig. 6.2

The results of this *Exercise* prove that when a voltage is applied across an inductor, current flow cannot instantly reach its final value of V/R. The time constant for this circuit can be calculated if the values of L and R are known.

Alternatively, the value of the time constant can be found by inspection of the graph. It is the time needed after switch-on for the current to reach 63% of its final value. After a time equal to four times the duration of the time constant, the current will have practically reached its steady value.

Back-E.m.f. in an Inductor

The slow rise of current through a large inductor when a voltage is connected across it is caused by the existence of **back-e.m.f.,** which is a voltage generated by the magnetic field of the inductor acting in the opposite direction to the applied voltage. The back-e.m.f. is particularly large when the rate-of-change of current flow is rapid, as occurs when a circuit containing an inductor is switched off.

Exercise 6.2
Connect the circuit shown in Fig. 6.3. The neon lamp will light only when the voltage across it rises to the order of 80V. Observe the light as the current is switched on and off.

    The behaviour of the neon bulb shows that large voltages, considerably greater than the supply voltage, are generated when the current through an inductor is switched *off.* In many circuits, it is necessary to take precautions to prevent damage to other components from this transient back-e.m.f. voltage. Diodes are for this reason commonly used to protect transistors which switch current in inductive loads, as will be seen in a later Chapter.

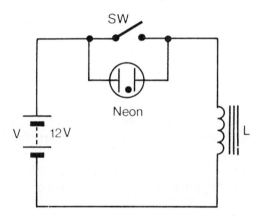

Fig. 6.3

Charge and Discharge in a Capacitor

While the voltage across the terminals of a capacitor is increasing, the capacitor is charging (*i.e.,* storing charge). When the voltage across a capacitor is decreasing, the capacitor is discharging, or releasing charge. Both of these processes take time, measured by the time constant $C \times R$ (expressed in seconds).

Exercise 6.3
Connect the circuit of Fig. 6.4(a), using a valve or FET voltmeter to measure the voltage across the capacitor. Take a reading of voltage for every second after switch-on, and plot a voltage/time graph. Compare this with the graph developed in *Exercise 6.1*.

    Now connect the circuit of Fig. 6.4(b). Set the signal generator to deliver a 1 kHz square wave of 2V amplitude peak-to-peak, and observe this trace on the oscilloscope. How does the shape of the trace compare with the shape of the graph line developed in 6.4(a)?

Examine the oscilloscope trace again with input frequencies of 100 Hz and 10 kHz, using 2V peak-to-peak square waves. Draw the resulting waveforms. Change the output of the signal generator to sine-wave and repeat the experiment, noting the shape of the output waveforms appearing on the oscilloscope.

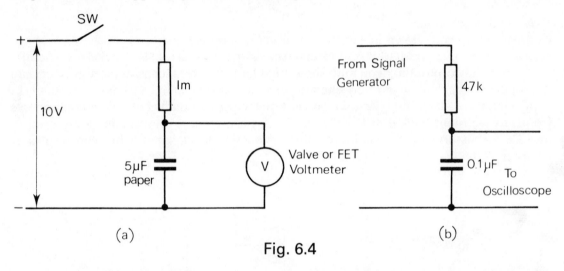

Fig. 6.4

The reason for the shape of the graph obtained in *Exercise 6.3* is that the voltage across the capacitor plates cannot change instantly when the voltage across the whole circuit is changed.

Another transient effect will be found if a capacitor and a resistor are connected as in Fig. 6.5. Again, the voltage between the capacitor plates cannot change instantly, so that

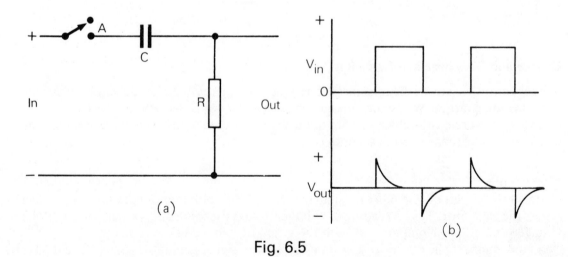

Fig. 6.5

when the switch is moved to Position A, voltage at the output at first equals battery voltage (so that the potential between the capacitor plates is zero volts), but then drops as the capacitor charges.

Both circuits of Fig. 6.4 are known as **integrating circuits,** that of Fig. 6.5 as a **differentiating circuit.** The action of either type of circuit on a square wave is determined by the value of the time constant of the circuit compared to the wave-time (or period) of the square wave.

SUMMARY

A circuit containing capacitors and/or inductors in addition to resistors will, for some time after a steady voltage is applied across it, behave as if the capacitors were open circuits and the inductors small-value resistors.

For a short time after a steady voltage has been either applied or removed, transient currents and voltages will exist in the circuit.

These effects will disappear after a time equal to approximately four time constants, but are very important in wave-shaping circuits.

The time constant is $C \times R$ seconds in a capacitor-resistor circuit and L/R seconds in an inductor-resistor circuit.

SINEWAVE-DRIVEN CIRCUITS

Reactance

Capacitors and inductors in d.c. circuits cause transient current effects *only when the applied voltage changes.* In an a.c. circuit, of course, the voltage is changing all the time, so that capacitors in such a circuit are continually charging and discharging, and inductors are continually generating back-e.m.f. In a *complex* circuit (as it is called) containing resistors, capacitors and inductors, an alternating voltage will exist across each component which is still proportional to the amount of current flowing through the component, however, so that a form of Ohm's law applies.

In the explanation which follows, the symbols $\widetilde{V}$ and $\widetilde{I}$ are used to describe the a.c. values (peak and r.m.s. respectively) of alternating *signal* frequencies. The symbols V and I have their usual meanings of peak and r.m.s. d.c. values.

In a resistor, $\widetilde{V} = R\widetilde{I}$; and the value of resistance found from the variant form of this equation, $R = \widetilde{V}/\widetilde{I}$, is the same as the d.c. value, V/I.

In a capacitor or an inductor, the ratio $\widetilde{V}/\widetilde{I}$ is called **reactance,** symbolised as X. Because this is a ratio of volts to amperes, the same units (ohms) are used to express its "resistance", but this resistance is a quantity of a very different kind. A capacitor may, for example, have a reactance of only 1k, but a d.c. resistance that is unmeasurably high. An inductor may have a d.c. resistance of 10 ohms, but a reactance of as much as 5k.

Unlike a resistance, too, the reactance of a capacitor or an inductor is not a constant quantity. A capacitor, for example, has a very high reactance to low-frequency signals and a very low reactance to high-frequency signals.

CAPACITIVE REACTANCE TABLES

Audio Frequencies

Frequency / Capacitance	20Hz	50Hz	400Hz	1kHz	5kHz	10kHz	20kHz
470 pF	Very High Values		847k	339k	68k	34k	17k
2n2	Very High Values		181k	72k	15k	7k	3k6
10n	796k	318k	40k	16k	3k	1k6	798R
47n	169k	68k	8k5	3k4	678R	339R	169R
220n	36k	14k	1k8	724R	145R	72R	36R
1µF	8k	3k	400R	160R	32R	16R	8R
10µF	800R	318R	40R	16R	Very Small Values ⋯		
100µF	80R	32R	4R	Small	Very Small Values ⋯		

Radio Frequencies

Frequency (Hz) / Capacitance	100k	470k	1M	5M	10M	20M	30M
10pF	160k	34k	16k	3k	1k6	800R	531R
22pF	72k	15k	7k	1k5	724R	362R	241R
100pF	16k	3k4	1k6	318R	159R	80R	53R
470pF	3k4	721R	339R	68R	34R	17R	Small
1n	1k6	339R	160R	32R	16R	Small Values	
4n7	339R	72R	34R	—	—	Small Values	
22n	72R	15R	7R	—	—	Small Values	
47n	34R	7R	—	—	—	Small Values	
0.1µF	16R	—	—	—	—	Small Values	

NOTE: Exact values of capacitive reactance have been omitted when calculation gives either very high (near 1M) or very low (a few ohms or less) values, since calculated values are not reliable at these extremes.
All figures have been rounded off, since exact values are never required.

The reactance of a *capacitor* ($\widetilde{V}/\widetilde{I}$) can be calculated from the equation:—

$$X_C = \frac{1}{2\pi \times f \times C}\ \textbf{ohms},$$

where f is the frequency of the signal in Hz and C the capacitance in farads. The tables above show the values of capacitive reactance which are found at various frequencies.

The reactance of an inductor varies in the opposite way, being low for low-frequency signals and high for high-frequency signals. Its value can be calculated from the equation:—

$$X_L = 2\pi \times f \times L\ \textbf{ohms},$$

where f is the frequency in Hz and L is the inductance in henries. The tables below show the values of inductive reactance which are found at various frequencies.

INDUCTIVE REACTANCE TABLES

Audio Frequencies

Frequency	20Hz	50Hz	400Hz	1kHz	5kHz	10kHz	20kHz
Inductance							
20 mH	Small Values		50R	126R	628R	1k3	2k5
50mH	Small Values		126R	314R	1k6	3k1	6k3
100mH	Small	31R	251R	628R	3k1	6k3	12k6
500mH	63R	157R	1k3	3k1	16k	31k	63k
1H	126R	314R	2k5	6k3	31k	63k	126k
10H	1k3	3k1	25k	63k	314k	Large Values	
100H	12k6	31k4	251k	— — — — Very Small Values			

Radio Frequencies

Frequency (Hz)	100k	470k	1M	5M	10M	20M	30M
Inductance							
10µH	Small	30R	63R	314R	628R	1k3	1k9
50µH	31R	148R	314R	1k6	3k1	6k3	9k4
200µH	126R	590R	1k3	6k3	12k6	25k	37k7
1mH	628R	2k9	6k3	31k4	62k8	126k	188k
2mH	1k3	6k	12k6	63k	126k	251k	Large
5mH	3k1	14k8	31k4	157k	— — — Large Values		
10mH	6k3	29k	63k	— — — — — Large Values			

NOTE: *The exact values have again been omitted when calculation gives either very high or very low values, since calculated values are not reliable at these extremes.*
All figures have been rounded off, since exact values are never required.

Exercise 6.4

Connect the circuit shown in Fig. 6.6. If meters of different ranges have to be used, changes in the values of capacitor and inductor will also be necessary. The signal generator must be capable of supplying enough current to deflect the current meter which is being used.

Connect a 5µF paper capacitor between the terminals, and set the signal generator to a frequency of 100 Hz. Adjust the output so that readings of a.c. voltage and current can be made. Find the value of $\widetilde{V}/\widetilde{I}$ at 100 Hz.

Repeat the readings at 500 Hz and at 1 000 Hz. Tabulate values of $X_C = \widetilde{V}/\widetilde{I}$, and of frequency f.

Now remove the capacitor and substitute a 0.5 H inductor. Find the reactance at 100Hz and 1000Hz as before, and tabulate values of $X_L = \widetilde{V}/\widetilde{I}$ and of frequency f.

Next, either remove the core from the inductor (if this is possible) or increase the size of the gap in the core, and repeat the measurements. How has the reactance value been affected by the change?

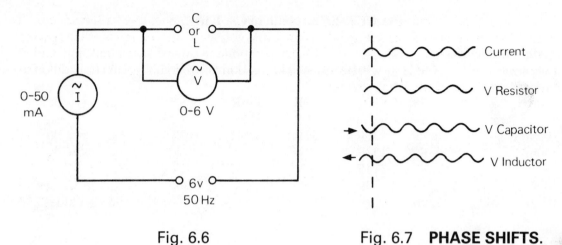

Fig. 6.6   Fig. 6.7   **PHASE SHIFTS.**

Phase Angle

There is another important difference between a resistance and a reactance, whether it be capacitive or inductive.

With the aid of a double-beam oscilloscope, the waveform of current through a resistor and of voltage across the resistor can be displayed together (see Fig. 6.7). This shows, as one might expect, that these waves coincide, with peak current coinciding with the peak voltage, and so on. But if this experiment is repeated with a capacitor or an inductor in place of the resistor, it will be seen from the Fig. that the waves of current and voltage do *not* coincide, but are a quarter-cycle (90°) out of step.

Comparing the positions of the peaks of voltage and of current, it will be seen that:—

*With a capacitor, the current wave **leads** (or precedes) the voltage wave by a quarter-cycle; and*

With an inductor, the voltage wave leads the current wave by a quarter-cycle.

Another way of saying the same things is:—

*With a capacitor, the voltage wave **lags** (or arrives after) the current wave by a quarter-cycle;*

With an inductor, the current wave lags the voltage wave by a quarter-cycle.

The amount by which the waves are out of step is usually defined as an angle, called the **phase angle.** The reason is that a coil of wire rotating in the field of a magnet generates a sine wave, with one cycle of wave being generated for every turn (360°) of rotation. One half-cycle thus corresponds to 180°, and one quarter-cycle to 90°.

Current and voltage are thus said to be *90° out of phase* in a reactive component such as a capacitor or an inductor.

Phasor Diagrams

It is only necessary to take a few measurements on circuits containing reactive components to see that the normal circuit laws used for d.c. circuits cannot be applied directly to a.c. circuits.

Consider, for example, a series circuit containing a 10μF capacitor C, a 2H inductor L and a 470-ohm resistor R, as in Fig. 6.8. With a 10V voltage $\widetilde{V}$ alternating at 50Hz applied to the circuit, the a.c. voltages across each component can be measured and added together ($\widetilde{V}_C + \widetilde{V}_L + \widetilde{V}_R$). It will be found that these measured voltages do *not* add up to the voltage $\widetilde{V}$ across the whole circuit.

Exercise 6.5

Connect the circuit shown in Fig. 6.8, with the values given above. Use either a high-resistance a.c. voltmeter or an oscilloscope to measure the voltage $\widetilde{V}_R$ across the resistor and the voltage $\widetilde{V}_C$ across the capacitor. Now measure the total voltage $\widetilde{V}$, and compare it with $\widetilde{V}_R + \widetilde{V}_C$.

Repeat the procedure, substituting the inductor L for the capacitor C and finding $\widetilde{V}_L$. $\widetilde{V}_R$ and $\widetilde{V}$. Again compare $\widetilde{V}$ with $\widetilde{V}_R + \widetilde{V}_L$.

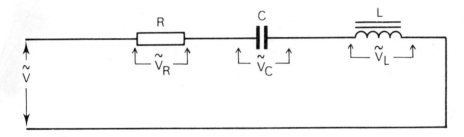

Fig. 6.8

The reason why the component voltages in a complex circuit do not add up to the circuit voltage when a.c. flows through it is the phase angle between voltage and current in the reactive component(s). At the peak of the current wave, for example, the voltage wave across the resistor will also be at its peak, but the voltage wave across any reactive component will be at its zero value (see Fig. 6.7). Measurements of voltage cannot however, indicate phase angle. They can only give the r.m.s. or peak values for each component, and the fact that these values do not occur at the same time cannot be allowed for by meter measurement. The result is that straight addition of the measured value will inevitably give a wrong result for total voltage, because of the time difference.

Phasor diagrams (often also called *vector diagrams*) are one method of performing the addition so that phase angle is allowed for.

In a phasor diagram, the voltage across a resistor in an a.c. series circuit is represented by the length of a horizontal line drawn to scale. Voltages across reactive components are represented by the lengths of *vertical* lines, also drawn to scale. If all the lines are drawn from a single point, as in Fig. 6.9(a), the resulting diagram is a phasor diagram that represents both the phase and the voltage of the wave across each component.

To represent the opposite effects that capacitors and inductors have on the phase, the vertical line representing voltage across an *inductor* is drawn *vertically upwards,* and the line representing voltage on a *capacitor* is drawn *vertically downwards.*

The phasor diagram can now be used to find the total voltage across the whole circuit. First, the difference between total upward (inductive) and total downward (capacitive) voltage is found, and a line is drawn to represent the size and direction of this difference. For example, if the inductive voltage is 10V and the capacitive voltage 7V, the difference is 3V drawn to scale in the direction of inductive reactance. If the inductive voltage were 10V and the capacitive voltage 12V, the difference would be 2V drawn to scale downwards in the capacitive direction.

The "net" reactive voltage so drawn is then combined with the voltage across the resistor in the following way. Starting from the point marking the end of the line representing the voltage across the resistor, draw a vertical line, as in Fig. 6.9(b), to represent the net reactive voltage in the correct direction, up or down. Then connect the end of this vertical line to the starting point (Fig. 6.9(c)).

The *length* of this sloping line will give the voltage across the whole circuit, and its *angle to the horizontal* will give the phase angle (φ) between voltage and current in the whole circuit.

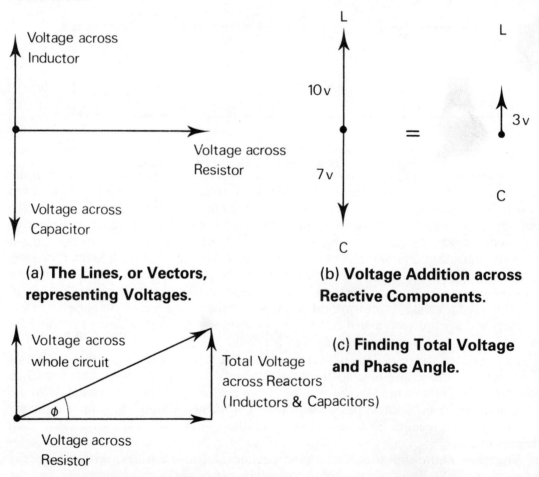

(a) **The Lines, or Vectors, representing Voltages.**

(b) **Voltage Addition across Reactive Components.**

(c) **Finding Total Voltage and Phase Angle.**

Fig. 6.9   **PHASOR DIAGRAMS for Complex Series Circuits.**

Impedance

A complex circuit which contains both resistance and reactance possesses another characteristic which is of great importance. This characteristic is known as **impedance**, symbolized by Z. Impedance is measured in ohms, and is equal to the quotient of the values $\widetilde{V}/\widetilde{I}$ for the whole circuit. Its value varies as the frequency of the signal varies.

When impedance is present, the phase angle between current and voltage is neither 90° (as it would be for a reactor) nor 0° (as it would be for a resistor), but some value in between the two. This angle can often be most easily found by using the device of a phasor diagram in a slightly different way, to form what is known as the *impedance triangle*.

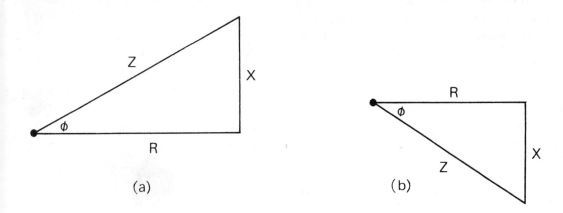

Fig. 6.10 **The IMPEDANCE TRIANGLE.**

In a phasor diagram constructed with this object, separate lines are drawn to represent the resistance R, the reactance X and the impedance Z. In a series circuit, the length of the horizontal line represents the total value of resistance in the circuit, and the vertical line its net value of reactance — upwards as before, for predominantly inductive reactance (Fig. 6.10a) and downwards for predominantly capacitive reactance (Fig. 6.10b).

With the values of R and X known and the angle between them a right angle, the Z line can be drawn in, representing the impedance value of the whole circuit. The angle of this line to the horizontal is the phase angle between current and voltage in the circuit.

Another way of working out the relationships between R, X and Z in a complex circuit is to express them by two algebraic formulae:—

$$Z = \sqrt{(X_L - X_C)^2 + R^2}$$

and
$$\tan\phi = \frac{X_L - X_C}{R}$$

where Z = total impedance, X_L = inductive reactance, X_C = capacitive reaction, and R = the resistance of the circuit as a whole. A pocket calculator covering a reasonably full range of mathematical functions can now be used to work out the values of circuit impedance and phase angle respectively.

SUMMARY

In an a.c. circuit, capacitors and inductors possess reactance, which is measured in ohms. The amount of reactance depends on the frequency of the a.c. and on the values of the various components.

A 90° phase difference between current and voltage exists in every reactive component.

A circuit which contains resistance as well as reactance possesses also impedance. Impedance, too, is measured in ohms, and has a phase angle somewhere between 0° and 90°. Both phase angle and the value of the impedance itself can be determined either algebraically or by the use of the impedance triangle.

Filters

It is possible to make good use of the way in which reactance varies when frequency is varied.

Fig. 6.11(a) shows a single *RC* circuit. At low frequencies, the reactance of the capacitor will be high, so that there is very little potential-divider action. At higher frequencies, however, the reactance of the capacitor will be less — with the result that the circuit now acts as a potential divider whose output signal voltage is less than its input signal voltage.

Such a circuit is called a *simple low-pass filter*, because it passes low-frequency signals unchanged, but both decreases the amplitude and changes the phase of signals of higher frequency.

Fig. 6.11(b) shows an equally simple *high-pass filter* based on the same principle. At high frequencies, the reactance of the capacitor is so small compared to the resistance value that there is practically no potential-divider action. At low frequencies, the reactance of the capacitor is so high that the signal is attenuated (*i.e.*, reduced in amplitude) and a phase shift takes place.

Fig. 6.11(c) shows a couple of more advanced filters whose graphs of amplitude versus frequency have a steeper slope than can be achieved by any simple *RC* filter.

Resonance

Part of the process of calculating the value of an impedance involves, as you have seen, finding the difference between the values of capacitive reactance, X_C, and inductive reactance, X_L. At low frequencies, X_C is large and X_L small; at high frequencies, X_C is small and X_L large. There must therefore be some frequency at which $X_C = X_L$.

This frequency is called the **resonant frequency,** or the **frequency of resonance,** of the *LCR* circuit in question. Its symbol is f_r.

A phasor diagram drawn for a series *LCR* circuit at its resonant frequency will clearly have a zero vertical component of reactance (Fig. 6.12). The impedance of the circuit will therefore be simply equal to its resistance. The same conclusion can be reached by working out the formula:—

$$Z = \sqrt{(X_L - X_C)^2 + R^2}$$

At its resonant frequency, therefore, an LCR circuit behaves as if it contained only resistance, and has zero phase angle between current and voltage.

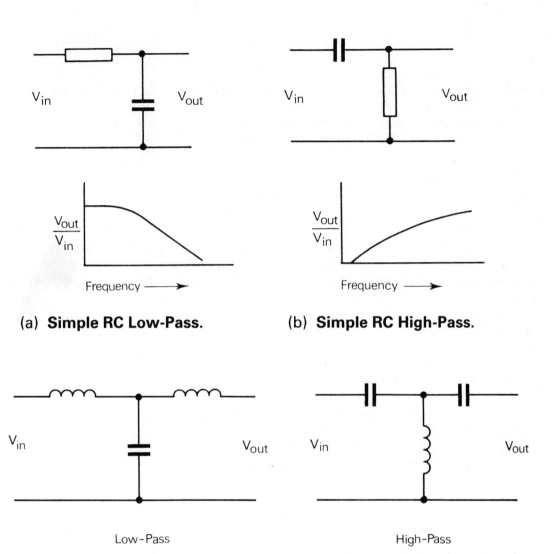

(a) **Simple RC Low-Pass.**   (b) **Simple RC High-Pass.**

Low-Pass   High-Pass

(c) **More advanced LC Filters.**
Fig. 6.11   **FILTERS.**

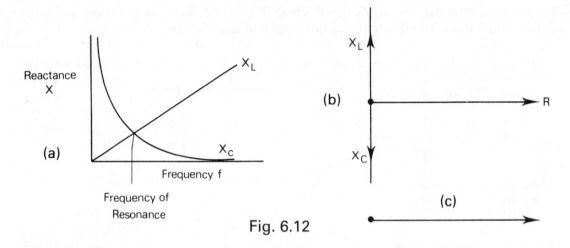

Fig. 6.12

RESONANCE.

(a) **The resonant frequency of a circuit containing inductance and capacitance is that at which the two reactances are equal.**
(b) **Since the reactance values are always opposite in direction, they cancel out on the phasor diagram.**
(c) **The impedance of a series *LCR* circuit at resonance is equal to its resistance only.**

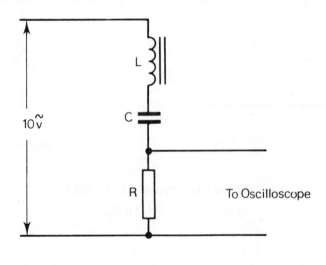

Fig. 6.13

Exercise 6.6

Connect the circuit shown in Fig. 6.13, with component values as follows:— $R = 1k$, $C = 0.1\mu F$ and $L = 80mH$. The resonant frequency of the circuit is about 1.8kHz.

Set the signal generator to 100Hz, and connect the oscilloscope so as to measure the voltage across the resistor R. This voltage will be proportional to the amount of current flowing through the circuit, because $V = R \times I$.

Now increase the frequency, watching the oscilloscope. The resonant frequency is the frequency at which current flow (and therefore the voltage across R) is a maximum. Note this frequency, and the value of the amplitude of the voltage across R at the resonant frequency.

Measure the voltages across L and across C by connecting the oscilloscope across each in turn. Note the value of these voltages.

Finally, use the oscilloscope to measure the voltage across the whole circuit.

Construct a phasor diagram for the voltages across R, C and L and confirm that this produces an answer for the total voltage. (Remember that the oscilloscope itself will disturb the circuit to some extent, and that the resistance of the inductor has not been taken into account in your calculation).

A **series-resonant circuit** consists of an inductor, a capacitor and a resistor in series. At the frequency of resonance, the circuit *as a whole* behaves as if only the resistor were present. Current flow in the circuit will be large if the voltage across the whole circuit remains constant, so that a large voltage exists across each of the reactive components in the circuit.

Generally, however, the voltage across both the capacitor and the inductor will be *greater* than the voltage across the whole circuit at the frequency of resonance. The ratio: $\tilde{V}_X/\tilde{V}_Z$, where $\tilde{V}_X$ is the voltage across a reactor and $\tilde{V}_Z$ is the voltage across the whole circuit, is called the **circuit magnification factor,** whose symbol is Q. Q can be very large at the frequency of resonance.

The frequency of resonance for a series circuit can be calculated by using the formula:—

$$f_r = \frac{1}{2\pi \sqrt{L \times C}}$$

where L is the inductance in henries, C the capacitance in farads, and f the frequency in hertz.

Example. What is the resonant frequency of a circuit containing a 200mH inductor and a 0.05μf capacitor?

Solution. Substitute the data in the equation: $f_r = \dfrac{1}{2\pi \sqrt{L \times C}}$ taking care to reduce both L and C to henries and farads respectively. Thus $L = 200 \times 10^{-3} = 0.2H$, and $C = .05 \times 10^{-6} = 5 \times 10^{-8}F$. Take 2π as being≈ 6.3.

Then $\qquad f_r = \dfrac{1}{6.3\sqrt{0.2 \times 5 \times 10^{-8}}}$

$\qquad\qquad\quad = 1587Hz$

Parallel Resonance

A circuit consisting of inductance, capacitance and resistance in parallel will resonate at a frequency given *approximately* by the same equation:—

$$f_r = \frac{1}{2\pi \sqrt{L \times C}}$$

At the frequency of resonance, a parallel resonant circuit behaves like a large value of resistance. Its actual value is $\frac{L}{C \times R}$, which is called the **dynamic resistance.** There is no phase angle between voltage and current at the frequency of resonance.

Exercise 6.7
Connect the parallel resonant circuit shown in Fig. 6.14 to the series resistor and the signal generator. Find the frequency of resonance, which for the component values shown will be about 2250Hz, and note that at this resonant frequency, the voltage across the resonant circuit is a maximum.

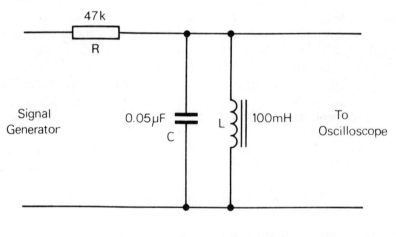

Fig. 6.14

Now connect another .05μF capacitor in parallel with C, and note the new frequency of resonance.

Remove the additional capacitor, and plot a graph of the voltage across the resonant circuit against frequency, for a range of frequencies centred about the resonant frequency. Observe the shape of the resulting curve, which is called the *resonance or response curve.*

Now add a 10k resistor in parallel with the resonant circuit, and plot another resonance curve, using the same frequency values. What change is there in the shape of the curve?

Repeat the experiment using a 1k resistor in place of the 10k one, and plot all three graphs on the same scale.

The result of these experiments will show that the addition of either capacitance or inductance to a parallel resonant circuit causes the frequency of resonance to become lower. The addition of resistance in parallel has little effect on the frequency of resonance, but a considerable effect on the shape of the resonance curve. The effect of adding a small value of resistance is to lower the peak of the resonance curve — as might be expected because the sum of two resistors in parallel is a net resistance smaller than either. In addition, however, the width of the curve is increased.

A resistor used in this way is called a *damping resistor*. Its effect is to make the resonant circuit respond to a wider range of frequencies, though at a lower amplitude. A damping resistor therefore increases the bandwidth of a resonant circuit, making the circuit less selective of frequency.

When a parallel resonant circuit is used as the load of a tuned amplifier, the tuned frequency is the resonant frequency of the parallel resonant circuit, and the amount of damping resistance employed will determine the bandwidth of the amplifier.

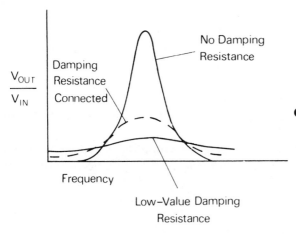

Fig. 6.15
The Effect of
DAMPING RESISTORS
on a Parallel Resonant Circuit.

SUMMARY

A circuit containing a capacitor and an inductor will have a resonant frequency (or frequency of resonance) at which the circuit has no phase shift.

A series resonant circuit will have low impedance at the resonant frequency — an impedance equal only to the circuit resistance. A parallel resonant circuit will have a high impedance at resonance (the dynamic resistance), and is used as the load for a tuned amplifier.

The shape of the resonance curve (amplitude plotted against frequency) for a parallel tuned circuit can be altered by adding damping resistors in parallel. This has the effect of lowering the peak of the curve and broadening its base.

CHAPTER 7
Waveform Generating and Shaping Circuits

Positive Feedback and Oscillation

The effects of *negative feedback* of a.c. signals on a voltage amplifier were described in Chapter 4. It will be recalled that negative feedback is achieved by subtracting a fraction of the output signal from the input signal of an amplifier. In practice, this is done by adding back the feedback signal *in antiphase,* so that feedback from an output which is in antiphase to an input is always negative unless some change of phase occurs in the circuit used to connect the output to the input (see later, under **RC Oscillators**).

If a signal which is *in phase* with the input is fed back, the feedback becomes *positive.* Positive feedback takes place when a fraction of the output signal is added to the signal at the input of an amplifier, so increasing the amplitude of the input signal. The result of positive feedback is higher gain (though at the cost of more noise and distortion) if the amount of feedback is small. If the amount of feedback is large, the result is oscillation.

An amplifier oscillates when:—

(a) The feedback is positive at some frequency; and

(b) The voltage gain of the amplifier is greater than the attenuation of the feedback loop (see Chapter 4 again to recall the concept of loop gain).

If, for example, 1/50th of the output signal of an amplifier is fed back in phase, oscillation will take place if the gain (without feedback) of the amplifier is more than 50 times, and if the feedback is still in phase.

Oscillator feedback circuits are arranged so that only one frequency of oscillation is obtained. This can be done by ensuring either:—

(a) That the feedback is in phase at only one frequency; or

(b) That amplifier gain exceeds feedback loop attenuation at one frequency only;

or

(c) That the amplifier switches off entirely between conducting periods.

Oscillator circuits are of two types. *Sine-wave oscillators* use methods (a) and (b) above for ensuring constant frequency operation. *Aperiodic* (or *untuned*) oscillators, such as multivibrators, make use of the third method. Oscillators are thus equivalent to amplifiers which provide their own inputs. They also convert into a.c. the d.c. energy from the power supply.

Sine-Wave Oscillators

A sine-wave oscillator consists of an amplifier, a positive feedback loop, and a tuned circuit which ensures that oscillation occurs at a single definite frequency. In addition, there must be some method of stabilising the amplitude of the oscillations so that the oscillation neither stops, nor builds up to such an amplitude that the wave becomes distorted by reason of bottoming or cut-off.

The most common types of sine-wave oscillator are those which operate at radio frequencies, such as are used in the local oscillators for superhet receivers which use LC tuned circuits to determine the oscillating frequency.

The Hartley Oscillator

Like most oscillator circuits, the Hartley oscillator exists in several forms; but the circuit of Fig. 7.1 is a much-used type. The tuned circuit $L_1\,C_2$ has its coil tapped to feed a fraction of the output signal back through C_4 to the emitter of Tr1. Since an output at the emitter is always in phase with the output at the collector, this feedback signal is positive. The base voltage of Tr1 is fixed by the values of the resistors R_1 and R_2, with C_1 acting as an a.c. by-pass capacitor.

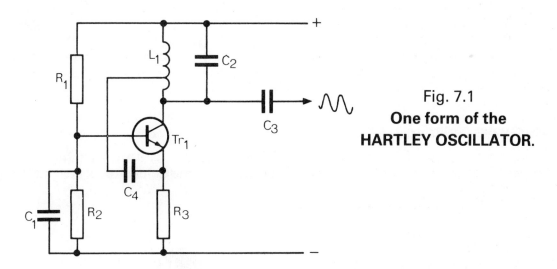

Fig. 7.1

One form of the

HARTLEY OSCILLATOR.

The amplitude of the oscillation is limited at the emitter, because the transistor will cut off if emitter voltage rises to a value more than about 0.5V below base voltage. The distortion of the wave-shape caused by this limiting effect is smoothed out by the "flywheel" effect of the tuned (or "tank") circuit $L_1\,C_2$, which produces a sine-wave voltage at the resonant frequency even when the current waveform is not a perfect sine-wave.

Irrespective of how its feedback is arranged, the Hartley oscillator can always be recognised by its use of a tapped coil. Its frequency of oscillation, as is the case with all oscillators using LC tuned circuits, is given by the formula:—

$$f_o = \frac{1}{2\pi\sqrt{LC}}$$

Example. What is the oscillating frequency of a Hartley oscillator which has a 15μH inductor and a 680 pF capacitor in its tuned circuit?

Solution. Substitute the data in the equation:—

$$f_o = \frac{1}{2\pi \sqrt{LC}}$$

Then

$$f_o = \frac{1}{2\pi \sqrt{15 \times 10^{-6} \times 680 \times 10^{-12}}}$$

$$= \frac{1}{2\pi \sqrt{10200 \times 10^{-18}}}$$

$$= \frac{1}{2\pi \times 1.009 \times 10^{-7}}$$

$$= 1.58 \times 10^6 \text{ Hz, or 1.6 MHz approx.}$$

Faults which can cause failure in an oscillator of this type include the following:—

(a) Bias failure caused by breakdown of either R_1, R_2, or R_3;

(b) A faulty by-pass capacitor;

(c) A leaky or o/c coupling capacitor C_4; or

(d) Faults in either C_2 or L_1.

C_2 should be of the silver-mica type of capacitor. Some ceramic capacitors will not permit oscillation because of "lossy action" — which means that the capacitor dissipates too much power to permit the circuit to resonate properly.

The Colpitts Oscillator

The example of this circuit shown in Fig. 7.2 demonstrates its basic similarity to the Hartley oscillator. Instead of using a tapped coil, however, the Colpitts oscillator employs

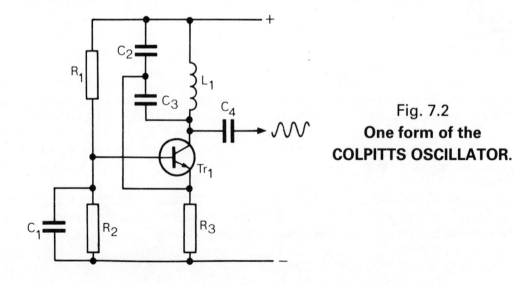

Fig. 7.2

One form of the

COLPITTS OSCILLATOR.

the combination of C_2 and C_3 to tap off a fraction of the output voltage to feed back into the base. This latter is biased and by-passed in the same way as in the Hartley circuit.

The same remarks about circuit operation, and about the several possible circuit configurations apply to the Colpitts as to the Hartley oscillator, but the formula for determining the frequency of oscillation is slightly different. Because the capacitors C_2 and C_3 are in series, it is the series combination C' (in which $1/C' = 1/C_1 + 1/C_2$) which tunes L_1 to give the output frequency. The formula therefore becomes:—

$$f_o = \frac{1}{2\pi\sqrt{L_1 C'}}$$

Example. What is the oscillating frequency of a Colpitts oscillator using an inductor of 25μH, and capacitors of 470 pF and 4700 pF in series?

Solution. The series capacitors have a total capacitance value, C', (in pF) such that $1/C'$

$= \frac{1}{470} + \frac{1}{4700}$. Therefore $C' = 427$ pF.

Substituting these data in the formula, one gets:—

$$f_o = \frac{1}{2\pi\sqrt{25 \times 10^{-6} \times 427 \times 10^{-12}}}$$

$$= \frac{1}{2\pi\sqrt{10675 \times 10^{-18}}}$$

$$= \frac{1}{2\pi \times 1.03319 \times 10^{-7}}$$

$$= 1.54 \times 10^7 \text{ Hz, or } 15.4 \text{ MHz}$$

Exercise 7.1

Construct the Colpitts oscillator shown in Fig. 7.2 with the following component values:—
$C_1 = 0.1\mu\text{F}$: $C_2 = 0.01\mu\text{F}$: $R_1 = 10\text{k}$: $R_2 = 1\text{k5}$: $R_3 = 1\text{k}$: $C_3 = 0.001\mu\text{F}$.
The inductor, L_1, should consist of 50 turns of 28-gauge enamelled copper wire close wound on a 10 mm diameter former fitted with a ferrite core. (Alternatively, the coil can be wound directly on a ferrite rod of the same diameter).

Check the circuit and connect to a 12V power supply. Connect the collector of the transistor to the Y-input of an oscilloscope, and link the negative line to the oscilloscope earth. Switch on, and adjust the oscilloscope to show the waveform from the oscillator. Measure the amplitude and frequency of the output wave.

Now observe the effects on the amplitude and frequency of oscillation of the following changes:—

(a) Increasing the supply voltage to 15V.
(b) Connecting an additional 0.001μF capacitor in parallel with L_1.
(c) Reducing bias by connecting a 2k2 resistor in parallel with R_2.
(d) Increasing bias by connecting a 22k resistor in parallel with R_1.
(e) Reducing feedback by connecting a 0.1μF capacitor in parallel with C_2.
(f) Increasing feedback by replacing C_2 by a 470 pF capacitor.

Note that changes (e) and (f) will both inevitably affect the frequency (if oscillation continues) because the capacitance of the tuned circuit has been changed in value.

Tuned-Load Oscillators

Oscillators of this type have a tuned circuit as the load of the transistor and use another component for feedback. The tuned-collector feedback oscillator shown in Fig. 7.3 uses a feedback winding placed physically close to the winding of L_1 to extract a fraction of the output signal, to invert its phase, and to feed it back to the base.

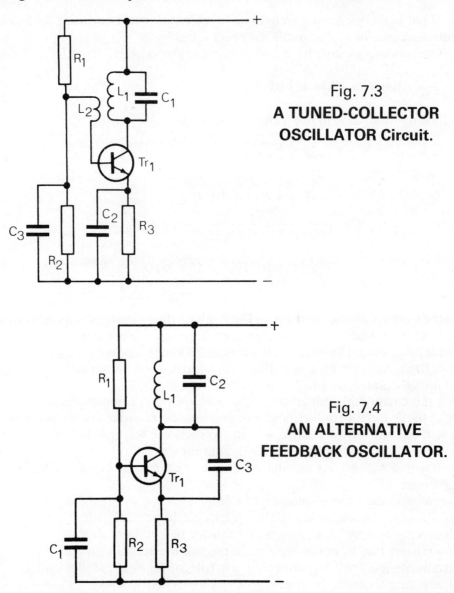

Fig. 7.3
A TUNED-COLLECTOR OSCILLATOR Circuit.

Fig. 7.4
AN ALTERNATIVE FEEDBACK OSCILLATOR.

Remember that the output of a single-transistor common-emitter amplifier is always phase-inverted, so that another inversion must be carried out if feedback is to be taken from the collector to the base.

Amplitude limitation is carried out in this circuit by the bottoming and cut-off action, and the output is smoothed into a sine-wave by the resonant oscillations of the tuned circuit.

Failure of the oscillator circuit shown in Fig. 7.3 can be caused by the by-pass capacitor C_2 going o/c, as well as by any of the biasing faults which can cause the Hartley oscillator to fail.

Another type of tuned-load oscillator is shown in Fig. 7.4. This circuit uses a capacitor of very small value, C_3, to feed back part of the signal from the collector to the emitter. This type of oscillator is commonly used at high frequencies as a local oscillator in TV or FM receivers.

Crystal Oscillators

The use of a quartz crystal in place of a tuned circuit in an oscillator gives much greater stability of frequency than can be achieved in the same conditions by any LC circuit.

There exists a great varity of crystal oscillator circuits, some of which use the crystal as if it were a series LC circuit, with others using it as part of a parallel LC circuit in which the crystal replaces the inductor.

The example of a crystal oscillator shown in Fig. 7.5 is a form of Colpitts oscillator, but with the crystal providing the frequency-determining feedback path and some of the 180° phase shift between collector and base. The choke L_1 acts as the collector load across which an output signal is developed and also contributes to the phase shift.

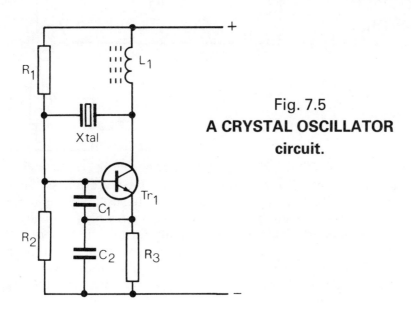

Fig. 7.5

A CRYSTAL OSCILLATOR

circuit.

In normal use, crystal oscillators are extremely reliable, but excessive signal current flowing through the crystal can cause it to break down and fail. The usual comments concerning bias and decoupling components apply here also.

Note that all the circuits for sine-wave oscillators can be constructed with MOSFET's in place of bipolar transistors. The use of MOSFET's has several advantages, particularly where crystal oscillators are concerned, because no input current is required at the gate of a MOSFET.

RC Oscillators

Oscillators required to operate at low frequencies cannot use *LC* tuned circuits because of the large size of inductor that would be needed. An alternative construction is the *RC* oscillator, of which Fig. 7.6 shows the basic outline of one type — known as the *phase-shift oscillator*.

Every *RC* potential divider must attenuate and shift the phase of the signal at the collector of the transistor. If the total phase shift at a given frequency is 180°, the signal fed back to the base will be in phase with the signal at the collector, and the circuit will oscillate.

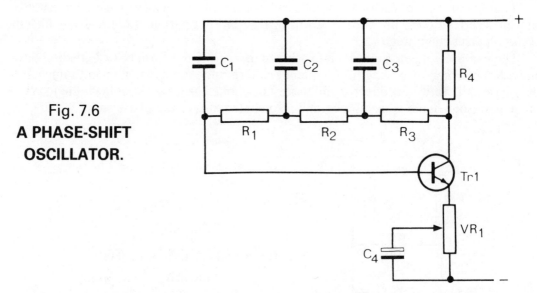

Fig. 7.6

A PHASE-SHIFT

OSCILLATOR.

The output waveform will not, however, be a sine-wave unless the gain of the amplifier can be so controlled that it is *only just enough* to sustain the oscillation. All *RC* oscillators therefore require an amplitude-stabilising circuit, which is usually provided by a negative feedback network. This network usually includes a component such as a *thermistor* whose resistance decreases as the voltage across it increases. In this way, an increase of signal amplitude causes an increase in the amount of negative feedback — which in turn causes the amplifier gain to decrease, so correcting the amplitude of oscillation.

Another type of *RC* oscillator is shown in outline in Fig. 7.7, in which only the components which determine frequency are labelled. This oscillator is known as the **Wien Bridge.** It will be noted that the circuit uses feedback to the non-inverting (in-phase) input of the amplifier.

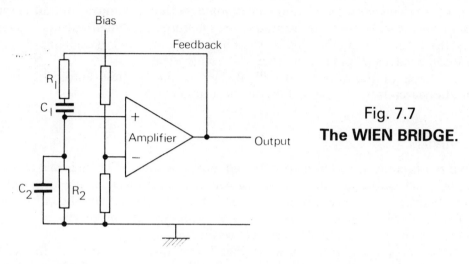

Fig. 7.7

The WIEN BRIDGE.

These RC circuits, also, require amplitude-stabilisation if they are to produce sine-waves of good quality, but they are capable of providing very low distortion figures (of the order of only 0.01%) by good design. An example of a Wien bridge oscillator circuit with provision for amplitude stabilisation is shown in Fig. 7.8. The amplifier itself is a 741 IC.

A distorted output from a *RC* oscillator is nearly always caused by failure of a component in the amplitude-stabilising circuit. Lack of output is generally due to a sudden loss of gain, such as could be caused by bias failure or by the failure of a decoupling capacitor.

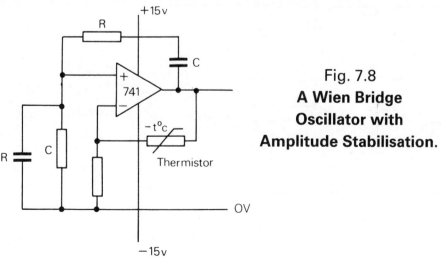

Fig. 7.8

A Wien Bridge

Oscillator with

Amplitude Stabilisation.

SUMMARY

Small amounts of positive feedback applied to an amplifier increase the gain of the amplifier. Larger amounts of positive feedback cause oscillation.

An oscillator requires three things:— An amplifier possessing sufficient positive feedback; A circuit sensitive to frequency; Some method of limiting output amplitude.

Sine-wave oscillators at radio frequencies can use *LC* tuned circuits or crystals to control the frequency of the sine-wave. Phase-shift or other *RC* circuits are used to generate sine-waves at audio and other low frequencies.

The shape of the waveform will always be poor unless automatic amplitude-stabilisation circuits are employed in oscillator design.

Multivibrators

Multivibrators comprise a family of three circuits, only one of which is in a true sense an oscillator. Each of the families consists of two amplifier stages having large amounts of positive feedback, so that the transistors are rapidly switched from the bottomed to the cut-off states and back again successively. The output waveforms produced by such rapid alternate switching are steep-sided square waves.

The basic configuration is shown in Fig. 7.9. At switch-on, one or other of the two transistors starts to conduct faster than does its fellow, by reason of minor differences in their circuits. Say this faster conductor is Tr1. Tr1 collector voltage will now fall faster than will that of Tr2. The fall is passed to Tr2 base as a negative-going signal serving to reduce its forward bias, and so its collector current. The collector voltage of Tr2 rises and is passed to Tr1 base as a positive-going signal, so that its conduction increases even further. This constantly-renewed regenerative action rapidly results in Tr1 becoming saturated (or *bottomed*) and Tr2 being cut-off.

The circuit remains in this stable state until it is forced to change.

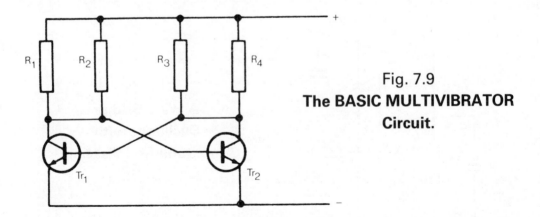

Fig. 7.9

The BASIC MULTIVIBRATOR Circuit.

The Bistable Multivibrator

A bistable is a multivibrator circuit which employs direct coupling throughout, and which remains in either of two states until it is triggered by a pulse which switches it over to the other state.

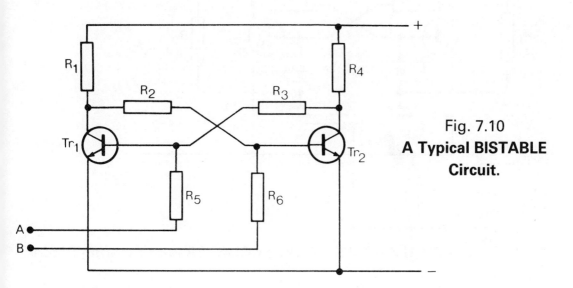

Fig. 7.10

A Typical BISTABLE Circuit.

Fig. 7.10 shows a typical bistable circuit using two transistors. In one stable state, Tr1 is conducting with Tr2 cut off. In the other state, the conditions are reversed. Both states are stable.

Trigger Pulses

Triggering can be achieved either by applying a negative pulse to the base of the transistor which is conducting or a positive pulse to the base of the transistor which is cut off. The arrangement shown in Fig. 7.11 uses *steering diodes* which cause a negative pulse to be automatically steered to the base of the transistor which is conducting, so that the circuit switches over. The action is as follows.

Say that Tr1 is conducting, with its base at about 0.5V and its collector voltage bottomed at about 0.2V. The connection of R_1 to the cathode of D1 ensures that this point is at a low voltage also — with the result that D1 can conduct if a negative pulse of low amplitude is received through C_1. At the same time, Tr2 is cut off, with its collector voltage high at about supply voltage. The connection of R_6 to the cathode of D2 biases this diode in the reverse direction, with about 6V on the cathode (given a 6V supply line) and about 0.2V on the anode.

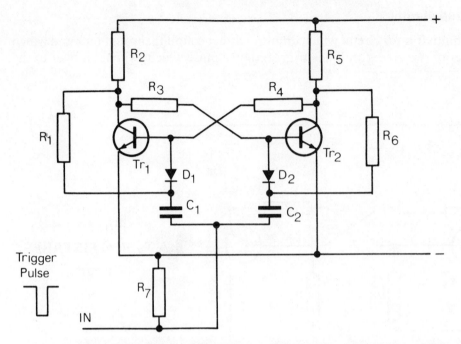

Fig. 7.11   **A BISTABLE SCALE-OF-TWO COUNTER with Steering Diodes.**

When a negative pulse of small amplitude (between 1V and 6V peak-to-peak) is injected into the circuit at the input, the only possible conduction path is through D1. Tr1 is therefore cut off, so switching the circuit. As usual, the positive feedback causes the change-over to be very rapid, being completed in something of the order of a microsecond or less.

The change-over also has the effect of switching over the bias voltages on the diodes, so that the next trigger pulse passes easily through D2 and switches the circuit back to its original state.

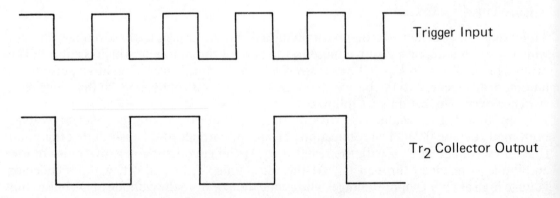

Fig. 7.12   **Bistable Counter Waveforms.**

Two complete trigger pulses are needed to cause the collector voltage of either Tr1 or Tr2 to go through the complete cycle, so that the circuit gives one complete pulse *OUT* for two trigger pulses *IN*. For this reason, it is often known as a *scale-of-two,* or *binary, counter.* The waveforms are shown in Fig. 7.12.

The Monostable Multivibrator

The monostable is a triggered multivibrator circuit which uses one capacitor coupling and one direct coupling in the positive feedback loop between the two transistors. An example is shown in Fig. 7.13.

In this circuit, current flowing through R_3 into the base of Tr2 keeps the transistor switched on, with its collector voltage consequently bottomed. Because the collector voltage of Tr2 is very low, the base voltage of Tr1, which is fed through the potential divider R_5-R_6, will be very low also. The circuit will remain in this state until it is triggered by a positive-going pulse at the input.

In the waveform sketches of the Fig. 7.13 monostable given in Fig. 7.14, the trigger pulse causes Tr1 to conduct and the positive feedback loop acts to cause the usual switchover action, with Tr1 now conducting and Tr2 cut off. C_2 then charges through R_3; and when the voltage at the base of Tr2 reaches about 0.5V, Tr2 starts to conduct and the positive feedback ensures that the circuit snaps back to its original state.

C1-R1 forms a differentiating network to ensure a sharp edge to the trigger pulse. D1 cuts off the negative-going pulse which C1-R1 produces, leaving only a positive trigger pulse.

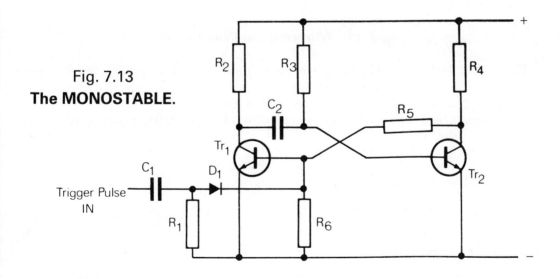

Fig. 7.13

The MONOSTABLE.

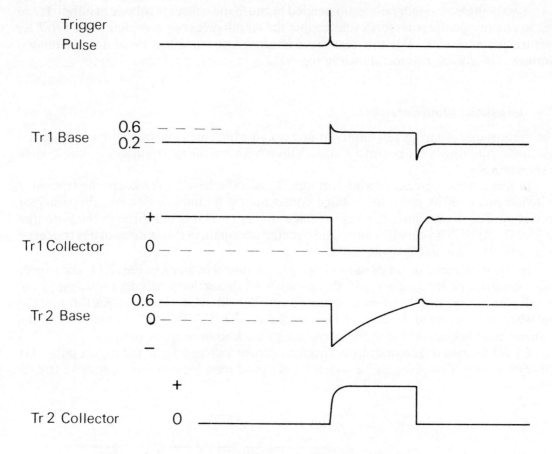

Fig. 7.14 **Monostable Waveforms.**

The base of Tr1 is isolated from any negative pulses (which would shorten the timed period) by the diode D1. The output pulse at the collector of Tr2 is a positive pulse having a duration of about $0.7\ C_2R_4$ (with C in farads and R in ohms).

Example. What is the output pulse time of a monostable with a 0.05µF coupling capacitor and a 68k bias resistor?

Solution. Pulse time $= 0.7\ CR$
$$= 0.7 \times .05 \times 10^{-6} \times 68 \times 10^3$$
$$= 2.38 \times 10^{-3}$$
$$= 2.4 \text{ ms (approx.)}$$

The Astable Multivibrator

The astable multivibrator is a two-transistor circuit which oscillates continuously, producing a wave of approximately square shape at the collector of each transistor. The most common form of the circuit is shown in Fig. 7.15, in which the waveforms produced are also shown on the same time scale, and with the same starting-times, so that the action of the circuit can be more easily followed.

Say that, as soon as the circuit is switched on, Tr1 conducts. The current flowing through R_1 will keep the collector voltage of Tr1 low, so that the base voltage of Tr2 is also held low because of the coupling capacitor C_1. C_1 now starts to charge, because of current flowing through R_2.

When the voltage at the base of Tr2 reaches about 0.5V, this transistor also starts to conduct. There is a positive feedback loop round Tr1 $\rightarrow C_1 \rightarrow$ Tr2 $\rightarrow C_2$, so that once Tr2 starts to conduct, the current increases very quickly until the collector voltage of Tr2 bottoms, when Tr2 ceases to amplify.

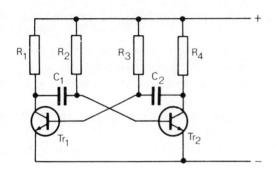

Fig. 7.15
The BASIC MULTIVIBRATOR
Circuit, and Waveforms.

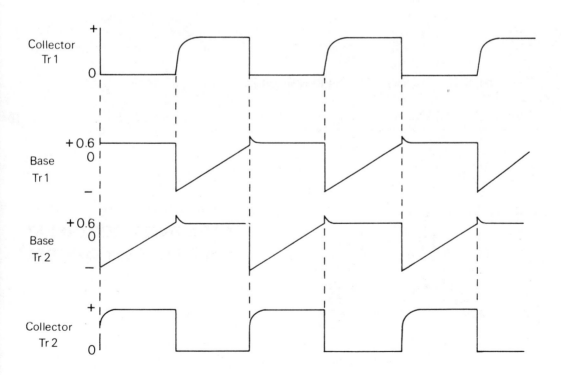

The sudden drop in voltage (almost 6V in the example given) at the collector of Tr2 will be transmitted by C_2 to the base of Tr1. This base was formerly at a voltage of about 0.5V, so a 6V drop will cause the base voltage to reach about −5.5V, cutting off Tr1 completely. C_2 now charges because of current flowing through R_3, until the voltage at the base of Tr1 reaches 0.5V. At that point Tr1 starts to conduct again and the positive feedback again causes another rapid switchover — this time to the state where Tr1 is bottomed and Tr2 cut off.

This swiftly-changing and self-perpetuating cycle continues automatically until power is switched off.

The important features of the flip-flop circuit are:—

(a) Each transistor spends most of the duration of every cycle either bottomed or cut off.

(b) The 100% positive feedback causes very rapid switching, so that the output waveforms have steep sides.

(c) The time between switchings is decided by the charging times of C_1 and C_2 through R_2 and R_3 respectively. The duration of a complete cycle is approximately $0.7 (C_1R_2 + C_2R_3)$, with the time expressed in μs if C is given in microfarads and in seconds if C is given in farads. R is always expressed in ohms.

(d) The frequency of the output is easily changed by making small changes in either the timing components C_1, R_2, C_2, R_3 or in the bias of the transistors.

Example. What is the approximate frequency of a multivibrator fitted with 0.001μF coupling capacitors and 56k bias resistors?

Solution. The duration of one cycle is approximately $0.7 (C_1R_2 + C_1R_3)$, with $C_1 = C_2 = 0.001$μF and $R_2 = R_3 = 56$k. Since in this Example $C_1R_2 = C_2 R_3$, it follows that $T = 2 \times 0.7 \times CR$.

Substituting, the formula becomes:— $2 \times 0.7 \times 0.001 \times 10^{-6} \times 56 \times 10^3$ seconds, and

$T = 7.84 \times 10^{-5}$ seconds, or 784 milliseconds.

Since $f = 1/T$,

$f = 1.27 \times 10^4$ Hz, or 12.7 kHz.

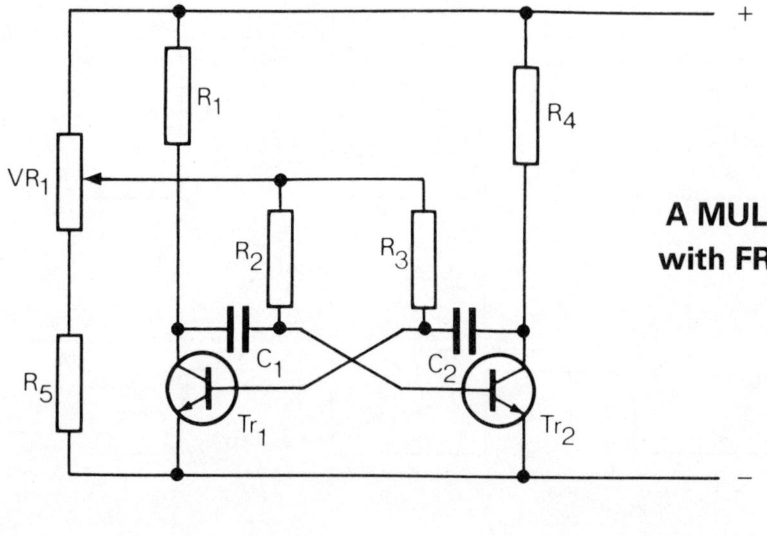

Fig. 7.16

A MULTIVIBRATOR CIRCUIT with FREQUENCY CONTROL.

The ease with which the frequency of the astable multivibrator can be varied is put to use in two ways. The first is to produce a circuit such as is shown in Fig. 7.16, in which circuit frequency can be varied at will by adjustment of the component *VRI.*

The second is to synchronise the oscillator to trigger pulses. A trigger pulse applied to one base causes the switchover to take place at the very moment of arrival of the pulse. The result is that the frequency of the astable will change to the frequency of the trigger pulse — provided that the frequency of this trigger pulse is *higher* than the free-running frequency of the astable circuit itself. A typical such circuit is shown, with its waveforms, in Fig. 7.17.

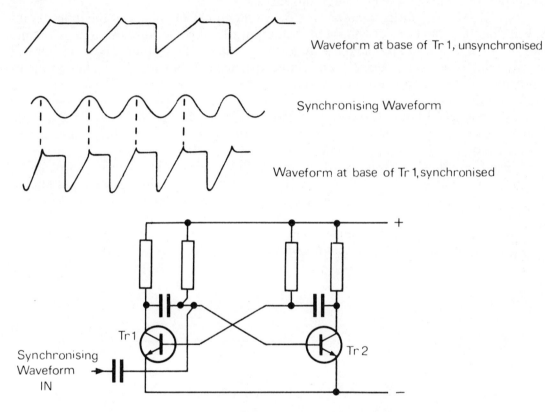

Waveform at base of Tr 1, unsynchronised

Synchronising Waveform

Waveform at base of Tr 1, synchronised

Synchronising Waveform IN

Tr 1

Tr 2

Fig. 7.17   **A SYNCHRONISED MULTIVIBRATOR.**

SUMMARY

Multivibrators are aperiodic oscillators, which means that they contain no tuned circuits.

In the usual two-transistor circuit, the large amount of positive feedback ensures that both transistors conduct for only a very short time. The normal state is to have one transistor conducting fully and the other cut off.

The astable multivibrator oscillates continuously; the monostable gives an output pulse of pre-determined duration when a trigger pulse is injected. In both types, the timing is determined by the time constant of a *CR* circuit or circuits.

The bistable multivibrator changes from one stable state to another every time a trigger pulse appears at the input.

Wave-Shaping Circuits

Wave-shaping circuits are circuits designed to alter the shape of waves other than sine-waves. The two most important such circuits are the *differentiating circuit* and the *integrating circuit.* Either can be constructed, in a simple form, by the appropriate connection of a single capacitor and a single resistor.

Fig. 7.18 shows a **differentiating** circuit. A sudden rise of voltage at the input, Point A, will cause an equal rise of voltage at the output, Point B, because the voltage on one plate of the capacitor will momentarily follow the voltage on the other. The capacitor will now charge, however, through R_1, until Point B reaches zero volts. This takes a time of approximately four times the time-constant of the circuit, R_1C_1 (with R in ohms, C in farads and time in seconds).

If the voltage at Point A should now suddenly drop, the output voltage will quickly drop by the same amount, and then more slowly return to zero as the capacitor discharges. The time required for the operation is again about four time-constants.

The differentiating circuit (as will be seen from Waveform B) produces sharp pulses, alternatively positive and negative-going, from inputs featuring sharp rises and falls of voltage. Its only effect on a sine-wave is to attenuate the wave and bring about a shift of phase.

Note that if the time-constant is made too long, the circuit behaves rather like a coupling network, so that the output becomes that of waveform C.

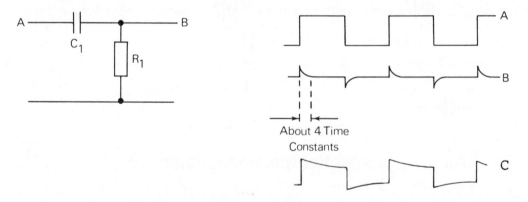

Fig. 7.18 **The DIFFERENTIATING CIRCUIT, and Waveforms.**

An **integrating** circuit is shown in Fig. 7.19. A sharp rise of voltage at the input. Point A. causes current to flow through the resistor R to charge the capacitor C. The charging will be complete in about four time-constants; but if the voltage is suddenly reduced before charging is complete, the capacitor will discharge, on the same time-constant, through R. An integrating circuit produces slowly rising or falling waveforms from sharp voltage changes — its action being thus the direct opposite of that of the differentiating circuit.

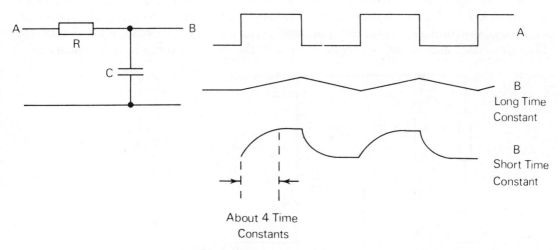

Fig. 7.19 **The INTEGRATING Circuit, and Waveforms.**

Note that a uni-directional pulse passing into an integrating circuit will produce a uni-directional output. The output of the differentiating circuit for the same input pulse is a pair of pulses whose average voltage value is zero.

The use of a differentiating circuit has already been illustrated in the timing action of the astable and monostable multivibrators. The names "differentiating" and "integrating" are taken from mathematical operations which change equations in a similar way.

The Sawtooth Generator

The ability of the integrator to convert a square wave into a wave with sloping sides makes it the natural basis for circuits used to generate the sawtooth waveform which produces **timebases.**

A simple timebase circuit is shown in Fig. 7.20. While Tr1 is conducting, the voltage at its collector is very low and C_1 is discharged. A negative-going pulse arriving (from an asymmetric astable multivibrator, for example) at the base of Tr1 will cut off Tr1, and C_1 starts to charge through R_2. This integrating action generates a slow-rising waveform which forms the sweep part of the sawtooth.

As the trailing edge of the pulse reaches its base, Tr1 is switched on again. C_1 rapidly discharges through Tr1 and causes the rapid flyback at the end of the sweep waveform.

Tr2 is an emitter-follower acting as a buffer stage to prevent the waveform across C_1 from being affected by the input resistance of circuits to which the sawtooth is coupled.

In such a simple circuit, the waveform across the capacitor will in practice be approximately a straight line if C_1 is only allowed to charge to a small fraction of the supply voltage. Thereafter, the waveform will tend to bend over towards the horizontal. To prevent this, it is important to make the time-constant $R_1 C_2$ much longer than the duration of the square pulse applied to the base of Tr1.

Sawtooth-generator circuits normally use considerably more elaborate circuits than that shown in Fig. 7.20, with the object of ensuring that the sweep voltage remains linear. One type of sawtooth generator uses constant-current circuits to replace R_2. Another, the Miller timebase, uses negative feedback to keep the sweep waveform truly linear.

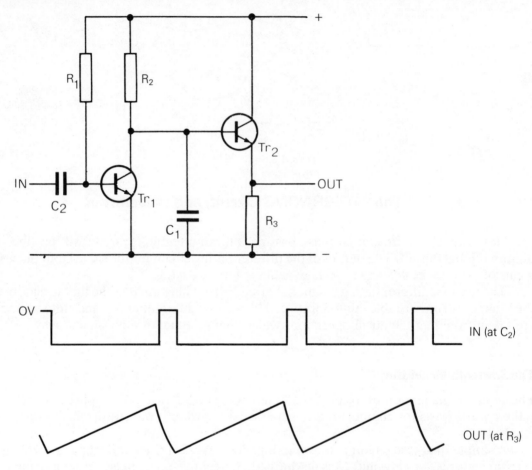

Fig. 7.20   **A Simple TIMEBASE, or SWEEP, Circuit.**

SUMMARY

Wave-shaping circuits do not change the shape of sine-waves, but affect all other waveforms.

Differentiating circuits form sharp pulses of voltage from the steep edges of square waveforms. Integrating circuits change steeply rising or falling voltages into smoothly changing waveforms.

The very important sawtooth waveform is generated by the action of an integrating circuit on a square-wave input.

CHAPTER 8

Miscellaneous Devices used in Electronic Equipments

I. Transformers

A transformer consists of two or more inductors so wound that their magnetic fields interact. (Note, however, that that definition does not hold good of the auto-transformer — for which see below).

Methods of causing the inductors to interact, or *couple*, in this way are to wind the coils very close to one another, and/or to put magnetic cores into the coils themselves.

The windings of a transformer are called **primary** and **secondary** respectively. Signals, which may be either a.c. or uni-directional, are applied to the primary winding(s) and induce output signals, which are always a.c. — never uni-directional — across the terminals of the secondary winding(s). A *steady* d.c. current flowing through the primary windings induces no output signal in the secondary windings at all.

The transformer works, as you will have supposed, on electromagnetic principles. The signal current flowing through the primary winding gives rise to a fluctuating magnetic field (ideally, a graph of magnetic field plotted against time would have exactly the same wave-shape as would a graph of signal current in the primary winding, also plotted against time). This fluctuating magnetic field *induces a signal voltage* in the secondary winding.

When the current is taken from the secondary winding by connecting a circuit to it, increased primary current must flow to provide the power which is being dissipated. If no current is taken from the secondary winding, current flow in the primary winding should be very small.

Some transformer constructions are illustrated in Fig. 8.1. Type (a) would be used at radio frequencies; type (b) at lower frequencies — with a cross-section through the construction shown at (d). Fig. 8.1(c) gives the symbols used to indicate various types of transformer core.

An Ideal Transformer

The ideal transformer would be one which suffers no loss of power when in use, so that no primary current at all would flow until secondary current was being drawn off. Large transformers in fact approach quite close to this ideal, which is used as the basis of all transformer calculations. In an ideal transformer:

$$\frac{\widetilde{V}_s}{\widetilde{V}_p} = \frac{n_s}{n_p}$$

where $\widetilde{V}_s$ = a.c. voltage, secondary; $\widetilde{V}_p$ = a.c. voltage, primary; n_s = number of turns of wire in the secondary winding; and n_p = number of turns of wire in primary winding.

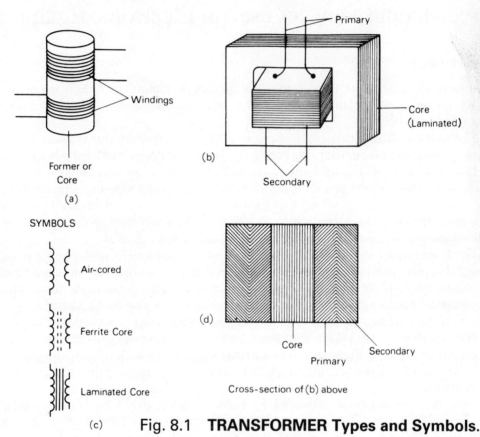

Fig. 8.1 **TRANSFORMER Types and Symbols.**

Example. A transformer has 7500 turns in its primary winding and is connected to a 250V 50 Hz supply. What a.c. voltage will be developed across its secondary winding if the latter has 500 turns?

Solution. Substitute the data in the formula:—$\dfrac{\widetilde{V}_s}{\widetilde{V}_p} = \dfrac{n_s}{n_p}$

Then $\dfrac{\widetilde{V}_s}{250} = \dfrac{500}{7500} = \dfrac{1}{15}$

So that $\widetilde{V}_s = \dfrac{250}{15} = 16.67V$, or say about 17V.

In practice, because no transformer is perfect, the output voltage would be somewhat less than 16V.

In the ideal transformer, the power input to the primary winding must be equal to the power taken from the secondary winding, so that:—

$$\tilde{V}_p.\tilde{I}_p = \tilde{V}_s.\tilde{I}_s \text{ or, re-arranging,} \frac{\tilde{V}_s}{\tilde{V}_p} = \frac{\tilde{I}_p}{\tilde{I}_s}$$

$$\text{and since } \frac{\tilde{V}_s}{\tilde{V}_p} = \frac{n_s}{n_p}, \text{ it follows that} \frac{\tilde{I}_p}{\tilde{I}_s} = \frac{n_s}{n_p}$$

The latter equation can also be expressed as $\tilde{I}_p.n_p = \tilde{I}_s.n_s$, an often convenient form which relates the signal current flows in the perfect transformer to the number of turns in each of the two windings.

Transformers are used in electrical circuits for the following purposes:—
1. Voltage transformation — converting large signal voltages into low voltages, or low signal voltages into large ones, with practically no loss of power.
2. Current transformation — converting low-current signals into high-current signals, or *vice versa*, with practically no loss of power.
3. Impedance transformation — enabling signals from a high-impedance source to be coupled to a low impedance, or *vice versa*, with practically no loss of power through mismatch.

Note carefully, however, that the transformer is a *passive* component which gives no power gain. If a transformer has a voltage step-up of ten times, it will also have a current *step-down* of ten times (assuming no losses *en route*).

Example. The secondary winding of a transformer supplies 500V at 1A. What current is taken by the 250V primary?

Solution. Since $\tilde{V}_s.\tilde{I}_s = \tilde{V}_p.\tilde{I}_p$

$$\text{then } 250 \times \tilde{I}_p = 500 \times 1,$$
$$\therefore \tilde{I}_p = 2A$$

The use of a transformer in impedance matching has been discussed in Chapter 5; the matching condition is:

$$\frac{R_s}{R_p} = \left(\frac{n_s}{n_p}\right)^2$$

This relationship can be usefully re-expressed in the form:—

$$R_p = \left(\frac{n_p}{n_s}\right)^2 \times R_s$$

so that the equivalent input resistance to signals entering a perfect transformer is

$$\left(R_L \frac{n_p}{n_s}\right)^2,$$

where R_L is the load resistance connected to the secondary winding. The equivalent circuit for a perfect transformer is therefore that shown in Fig. 8.2.

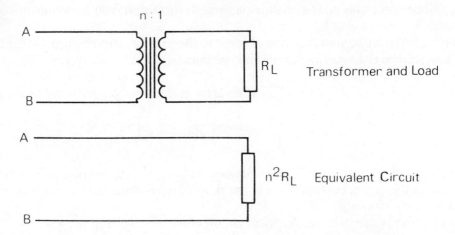

Fig. 8.2   **Equivalent Circuit of a Perfect Transformer.**

Transformer Losses

The types of power loss which a transformer can suffer are the following:—
1. I^2R losses caused by the resistance of the windings;
2. Eddy-current and stray inductance losses caused by unwanted magnetic interactions;
3. Hysteresis loss arising from the core material, if a core is used.

Taking these in turn, I^2R (or *joule*) losses are those which are always incurred in any circuit when a current, steady or a.c., flows through a resistance. These losses can be reduced in a transformer by making the resistance of each winding as low as possible consistent with the correct number of turns and the size of the transformer.

Joule losses are generally insignificant in transformers used at radio frequencies; but they will cause overheating of mains transformers, particularly if more than the rated current is drawn or if ventilation is inadequate.

Stray inductance and *eddy current losses* are often more serious. An ideal transformer would be constructed so that all the magnetic field of the primary circuit coupled perfectly into the secondary winding. Only toroidal (ring-shaped) transformers come close to this ideal (and even those in the smaller sizes only). In practice, there arises from the primary winding a strong alternating field which is detectable at some distance from the trans-former, causing a loss of energy by what is termed *stray inductance*.

In addition, the alternating field of the primary can cause stray voltages to be induced in any conducting material used in the core or casing of the transformer, so that unwanted currents, called *eddy-currents,* flow. Since additional primary current must flow to sustain these eddy-currents, they cause a loss of power which can be significant.

The problem of eddy-currents in the core is tackled in two ways:—
1. The core is constructed of thin laminations clamped together, with an insulating film coating on each to lessen or eliminate conductivity; and
2. The core is constructed from a material possessing high resistivity, such as ferrite.

The third type of loss, called *hysteresis loss,* occurs only when a magnetic core is used. It represents the amount of energy which is lost when a material is magnetised and de-magnetised. This type of loss can be minimised only by careful choice of the core material for any particular transformer.

Hysteresis losses will, however, increase greatly if the magnetic properties of the core material change, or if the material becomes magnetically saturated. The following precautions should therefore be taken in connection with transformers:—
1. Do not dismantle transformer cores unnecessarily, nor loosen their clamping screws;
2. Never bring strong magnets near to a transformer core;
3. Never pass d.c. through a transformer winding unless the rated value of the d.c. is known and is checked to be correct.

Transformer Construction

The way in which transformers are constructed depends greatly on the frequency range for which they are intended. The following conditions are samples only of the considerations which may apply.

Mains Supply. Mains frequency is low (50 to 60 Hz) and fixed, and a substantial core of silicon-iron is required. The core must be laminated, and hysteresis loss can be reduced to negligible proportions by careful choice of a core material. Where an external magnetic field is especially undesirable (as in audio amplifiers and cathode ray oscilloscopes), a toroidal core can with advantage be used.

Audio-frequency Range. The core material must be chosen from materials causing only low hysteresis loss because of the higher frequencies which will be encountered, and the windings must be arranged so that stray capacitance between turns is minimised. In general, any flow of d.c. is undesirable.

Lower-range Radio Frequency. In this range, the losses from laminated cores are unacceptably high, so that ferrite cores must be used. Because of the high frequencies involved, a small number of turns is sufficient for each winding. Stray fields are difficult to control, so that *screening* (see below) is often needed.

Higher-range Radio Frequency. Only air cores can be used in this range, and "coils" may actually comprise less than one full turn of wire. They may even consist of short lengths of parallel wire. Unwanted coupling becomes a major problem, so that the physical layout of components near the transformer assumes great importance.

Two variations on transformer construction are **tapping** and **bifilar winding.**

A *tapping* is a connection made to a selected part of the wire of a winding so that different numbers of turns may be selected for different jobs. Mains transformers, for example, will have several tappings on the primary winding so as to be able to handle different values of mains voltage. Multiple-tapped secondary windings — Fig. 8.3(b) — can also be used to provide several different ratios from one transformer, so that different secondary voltages or matching ratios can be obtained.

A centre-tapped secondary winding — Fig. 8.3(a) — is a good way of obtaining phase-inverted signals for audio amplification or for rectification. This principle can be extended to the auto-transformer, which is a single-tapped winding equivalent to the use of a double-wound transformer with one end of the primary connected to one end of the secondary. The ratio of input/output voltages and currents still follows the normal transformer relationships. An auto-transformer with a variable tapping position (such as the *Variac*) is used for providing variable voltage a.c. supplies. Note, however, that such transformers provide no isolation between their primary and secondary windings.

Bifilar winding — Fig. 8.3(c) — is a method of providing very close coupling between primary and secondary windings, particularly useful in audio transformers. In this method of construction, the primary and the secondary turns are wound together, rather than in separate layers.

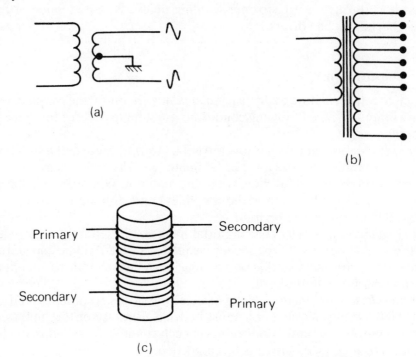

(a)

(b)

(c)

Fig. 8.3   Types of TRANSFORMER WINDINGS.

Shielding, or Screening

Components such as transistors and inductors may need to be shielded from the fields which are radiated by transformers. Electrostatic screening is comparatively easy, for any earthed metal will screen a component from the electrostatic field of a transformer (though with high frequencies a metal box which is almost watertight may have to be used).

Electromagnetic screening, on the other hand, calls for the use of high-permeability alloys such as *mu-metal* or *super-Permalloy*. Surrounding a component with such a material ensures that no magnetic fields from outside the box can penetrate into it.

Exercise 8.1
Using a transformer of known turns ratio, preferably a type using a tapped secondary winding, connect the circuit shown in Fig. 8.4. Measure the a.c. input and output voltages

for each set of taps, and find the values of $\widetilde{V}_s/\widetilde{V}_p$. Compare these values with the known values of the turns ratio.

An effective component to use in this *Experiment* is a toroidal core with a 240V primary winding, obtainable from most Educational Suppliers.

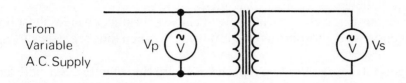

From
Variable
A.C. Supply

V_p

V_s

Fig. 8.4

Transformer Faults

The following are common transformer faults, with hints on how to detect and remedy them:—

(a) Open-circuit windings, which can be detected by ohmmeter tests. A winding may also acquire high resistance, typically 100k instead of 100 ohms.

(b) Short-circuit turns, which are difficult to detect because the change of resistance is very small. S/c turns will cause an abnormally large primary current to flow when the secondary is disconnected, so that mains transformers overheat and transformers operating at high frequencies fail completely. This is a fault which particularly affects TV line output transformers. The most certain test and cure is replacement by a component known to be good.

(c) Loose, damaged or missing cores. Loose cores will cause mains transformers to buzz and overheat. Cracked or absent ferrite cores in radio-frequency transformers will cause mis-tuning of the stage in which the fault occurs.

SUMMARY

A transformer transfers signals (but not their d.c. level) from a primary winding to a secondary winding. The signal voltage can be stepped up or down, depending on the relative number of turns used in the two windings. Impedance matching can also be achieved by means of a transformer.

The type of construction of a transformer, and its core material if used, must be carefully chosen to suit the range of frequencies which the transformer is being designed to handle.

II. The Cathode-Ray Tube (CRT)

The cathode-ray tube operates by harnessing the movement of electrons in a vacuum, and on the following principles:—

1. Electrons are released into a vacuum when a number of different materials are heated to certain high temperatures.

2. Electrons, being negatively charged, are attracted to positively-charged metal plates and are repelled from negatively-charged plates.

3. Moving electrons constitute an electric current, and so can themselves form part of a circuit.

4. The direction in which a stream of electrons moves can be changed by applying to it one or more magnetic fields.

5. Moving electrons carry energy, and so will cause substances called phosphors (which have no connection with phosphorus) to glow brightly when they are struck by an electron beam.

Cross-sectional diagrams of two typical CRTs are shown in Fig. 8.5. The one marked (a) is an instrument tube, while (b) is a wide-angle tube used in black-and-white television. The function of the various parts is as follows, and is illustrated in Fig. 8.6.

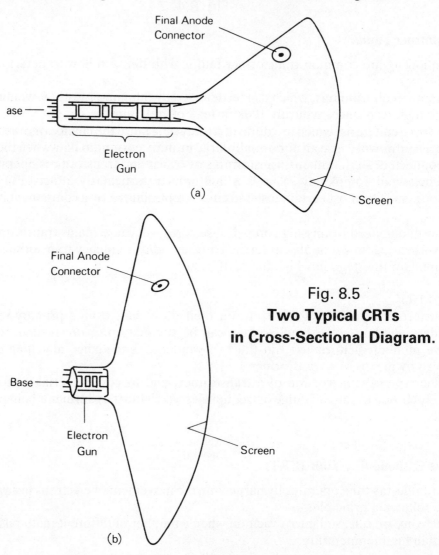

Fig. 8.5
**Two Typical CRTs
in Cross-Sectional Diagram.**

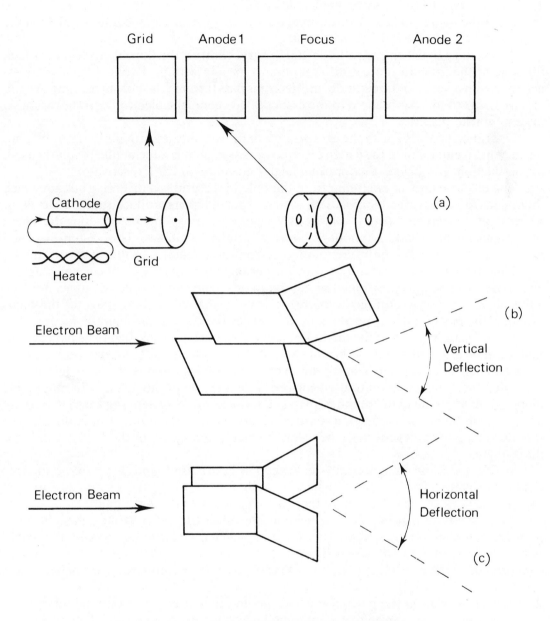

Fig. 8.6 **The ELECTRON GUN of a CRT.**

The cathode is a nickel cup, coated at its closed end with a mixture of materials which emit electrons when at red heat. Heating is carried out electrically, using a molybdenum or tungsten wire which has to be coated with aluminium oxide to insulate the heater from the cathode. Failure of this insulation is a common CRT fault.

Surrounding the cathode is another, larger, metal cup called the *grid,* or *control grid.* This has a small (0.025 mm or less) hole at its centre. The heater, cathode and grid constitute the source of the electron beam and require four connections — two for the heater, and one each for the cathode and grid.

The voltage between the cathode and the grid controls the flow of electrons through the hole in the grid. In the cut-off condition, typically with grid voltage 15 to 85 volts negative with respect to the cathode, no electrons pass through the hole in the grid. At grid voltages of zero to – 5V relative to the cathode, however, the electron current reaches a maximum (full-beam).

Operation of a CRT with the grid *positive* to the cathode is normally undesirable, but it can help an elderly tube to sustain electron emission, and is a technique regularly used, in conjunction with higher-than-normal heater currents, in CRT reactivators.

The electron stream emerging from the hole in the grid is a diverging stream which then needs to be converged, or *focused*, so that a spot of light is produced at the exact point where it hits the screen. Focus is achieved by placing at appropriate places along the length of the gun metal cylinders (anodes) carrying different voltages. This system is called *electrostatic focusing*. It is more commonly used nowadays than is an alternative technique called *electromagnetic focusing,* in which a permanent magnet or a focus coil through which d.c. is flowing is positioned along the neck of the tube. Since the focus must be adjustable, some provision has to be made for altering either the voltage of the focus cylinder, the position of the permanent magnet, or the current through the focus coil.

Once focused by any of the methods mentioned, the beam has then to be deflected so that it can be directed at any part of the screen. Electrostatic CRTs used in oscilloscopes use metal deflector plates to achieve this. The pair of plates situated closer to the cathode are called the *Y-plates,* and are used for *vertical* deflection of the beam. The other pair, mounted at 90° to the plane of the Y-plates, are called the *X-plates,* and cause *horizontal* deflection of the beam. Deflection sensitivity, measured as the number of millimetres of spot deflection per volt difference between the plates, is greater for the Y-plates than for the X-plates.

In TV and radar, magnetically-deflected CRTs are used, and there are no internal deflecting plates. The magnetic deflection coils form an external component located around the neck of the tube, where they are supplied with current signals.

Finally, after focusing and deflection, the electron beam strikes the phosphor material deposited on the screen. This material, which is an insulator, is generally coated with a thin film of aluminium which acts in two ways:
1. It provides a metal contact so that a high (positive) accelerating voltage can be applied to it; and
2. It reflects light from the phosphor which would otherwise be lost into the tube.

Electrons can penetrate this aluminium layer quite easily — a fact which makes the gains to be had from using such a layer easily exceed the losses.

The voltage which is applied between the cathode and the screen (the *final anode connection*) is called the *EHT* (which stands for Extra High Tension). It has the effect of accelerating the electrons towards the screen. The greater this acceleration, the brighter will be the spot when the full beam current strikes a phosphor dot on the screen.

The value of the accelerating voltage also has an effect on the deflection sensitivity.

At large values of EHT, much more deflection effort, be it voltage between plates or current through coils, is needed to achieve the same number of millimetres of deflection than is needed at lower EHT values. Electrostatically-deflected tubes suffer rather more from this problem than do magnetically-deflected CRTs.

The Choice of Deflection Methods

Instrument CRTs invariably employ electrostatic deflection. This method of deflection is well suited to signals which can range in frequency from d.c. to several MHz, because the deflection plates behave in a circuit as if they were a small-value capacitance. Since no steady current is drawn by the plates, they can be supplied with signals from a voltage amplifier.

The use of plates for deflection, however, limits the amount of EHT which can be used, because large EHT voltages reduce deflection sensitivity to unacceptably low values. Bright traces, which are needed when very fast deflection is required, are obtained by further accelerating the electron beam *after deflection*. The technique is called *PDA*, or *post-deflection acceleration*. A CRT using this technique requires two EHT supplies.

Television and radar CRTs need screens of much larger size, and generally use a much larger proportion of those screens themselves, than do instrument tubes; so much higher beam currents are needed to produce an acceptable level of brightness over the whole screen. Acceleration voltages of 8 to 25kV are common, depending on the size of the tube and whether the set is monochrome or colour — the highest accelerating voltages being required by large colour tubes.

For such high beam currents and acceleration voltages, the technique of magnetic deflection is appropriate because the deflection frequency itself is either fixed or only slightly variable, so that the coils can be designed for optimum operation at that frequency.

Typical Operating Voltages

The Table below shows a typical range of voltages encountered on the CRT electrodes used in different applications (though it should be noted that values may in practice differ significantly from those quoted).

Note also that in the oscilloscope it is convenient to use a combination of negative and positive supplies to obtain the high potential required between the cathode and the final anode. This allows the grid electrode to operate near to earth potential.

	Cathode	Grid	First Anode	Focus Anode	Final Anode
Monochrome	+80V	+20V	+300V	up to +350V	10 – 15kV
Colour	+150V	+40V	+1500V	up to +4kV	25kV
Oscilloscope	−100V	0V	+100V	0 to −200V	2 – 4kV

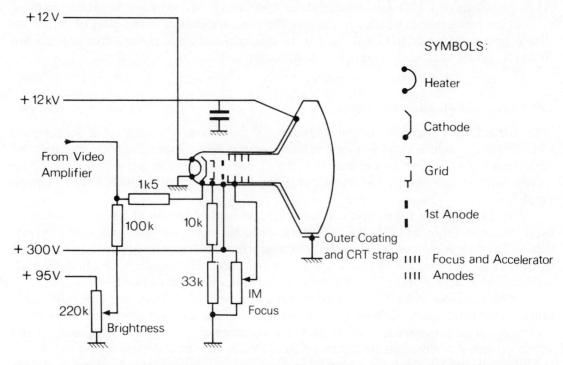

Fig. 8.7   Some of the Circuitry serving the CRT of a Portable Monochrome Television Receiver

CRT Faults

The following faults in a CRT are common:—

1. *Low Maximum Brightness* — the causes of which could be either low EHT, faulty voltage supply to the grid or low cathode emission (in an old tube).

2. *Uncontrollable Brightness* — caused by shorts between either heater and cathode or grid and cathode.

3. *Deflection Irregularities* — usually caused by amplifier failures, but if an instrument tube is dropped or sharply knocked, a deflection plate can be loosened or even detached.

4. *No Trace* — probably caused by amplifier or power supply failure, or by an o/c tube heater.

5. *Other Tube Faults* include misaligned grid, o/c connections, and leakage of air into the tube. A leaking ("down-to-air") tube can be detected if the *gettering* (the name used to describe the normally silvery deposit at the neck of the tube) has turned white.

Exercise 8.2.
Examine an assortment of electron guns from both instrument and television CRTs, and note the position of the various electrodes.

Exercise 8.3.
Use either a specially set-up instrument tube, or press into service a spare oscilloscope. If an oscilloscope is used, take great care to identify the correct connections.

With all supplies to the tube switched off and all leads shorted one after another to earth in order to discharge any capacitors, attach the leads of a high-resistance voltmeter to the cathode (+) and grid (−). Replace the covers so that no points where high voltages will be present can be touched when the tube is switched on. (It should be made *impossible* for you or anyone else to touch any part of the voltmeter leads save where they are properly covered by insulation).

Switch on, and note the action of the brilliance (*Brightness*) control. If a photographic exposure meter is available, plot a graph of screen, or spot, brightness against bias voltage.

SUMMARY

The cathode-ray tube (CRT) is an air-evacuated tube which contains an electron gun capable of producing a beam of electrons. This electron beam can be focused and deflected to produce a spot on a phosphor screen.

The voltage between grid and cathode controls the brightness of the spot, and the voltage on the focus anode controls the focus (diameter) of the spot. Magnetic focus coils or permanent magnets are sometimes used to achieve focus.

The beam is deflected either by voltages set up on metal plates within the tube ("electrostatic deflection"), or by the magnetic fields produced when currents are passed through external coils ("magnetic deflection"). Electrostatic deflection is used in small tubes such as instrument tubes, while magnetic deflection is used for large tubes intended for TV and radar.

CHAPTER 9
Logic Circuits and Displays

The operation of **digital** circuits is controlled by two voltage levels only — either low voltage, referred to as **Logic 0,** or high voltage, referred to as **Logic 1.** The terms "high" and "low" are comparative only, since the "high" voltage is often as little as +5V, and the "low" about 0.2V.

By contrast, signals such as sine-waves (*see Fig. 9.1*) constitute **analogue** signals. They have a continuously varying amplitude, lying anywhere between the peak values of the sine-wave voltage or current.

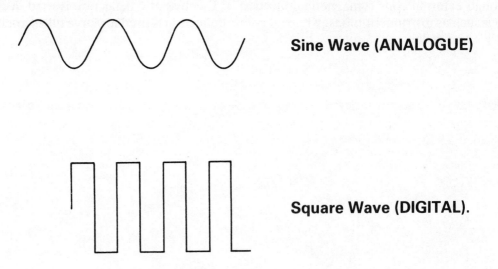

Sine Wave (ANALOGUE)

Square Wave (DIGITAL).

Fig. 9.1

Two conventions define the levels of logic signals. These are shown in Fig. 9.2 in **positive logic,** the most positive voltage level represents Logic 1. In **negative logic,** the reverse is the case, with the *most negative* voltage representing Logic 1.

Positive and Negative Logic.

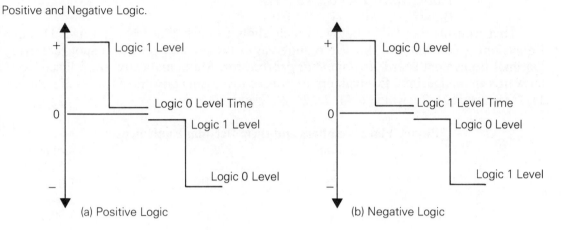

Fig. 9.2 **POSITIVE and NEGATIVE LOGIC.**

All digital counting and computing circuits use the figures 0 and 1 — and those figures only — in what is called the **binary counting scale.** Table 9.1 below shows how decimal numbers are converted into binary, and vice versa. For the purposes of machine control, Logic 1 represents switch-on, and Logic 0 switch-off. It is as simple as that.

TABLE 9.1

DECIMAL-TO-BINARY CONVERSION

Write down the decimal number you wish to convert. Say it is	1065	
Divide by two; write the result below and the remainder (0 or 1) at the side	532	1
Now divide the result by two again, once more placing the result below and the remainder at the side	266	0
	133	0
	66	1
	33	0
Go on doing this until the last possible figure has been divided, leaving	16	1
zero and a remainder of 1. Thus:—	8	0
	4	0
	2	0
	1	0
	0	1

Now read off *the remainders* in order *from the foot of the column upwards,* and you get the binary number. In the example given, the binary equivalent of 1065 is 10000101001.

BINARY-TO-DECIMAL CONVERSION

Write out the binary number and set above each of its digits its proper *Place Number*, starting with Place No. 0 at the right-hand digit of the binary number and working to the left from there. Thus in the Example given:—

Place No. *10 9 8 7 6 5 4 3 2 1 0*

Binary No. 1 0 0 0 0 1 0 1 0 0 1

Then consult the Table below, which allots to each Place No. its own Decimal Equivalent. (You will find the Table quite easy to remember once you spot that every Decimal Equivalent is *exactly double its predecessor*. Mathematically, from Place No. 1 leftwards all the Decimal Equivalents are consecutive rising powers of two — 2^0 (which is 1), 2^1 (which is 2), 2^2 (which is 4), 2^2, 2^3, 2^4, 2^5 etc.

Binary Place Numbers and their Decimal Equivalents

Place No.	Decimal	Place No.	Decimal
0	1	9	512
1	2	10	1 024
2	4	11	2 048
3	8	12	4 096
4	16	13	8 192
5	32	14	16 384
6	64	15	32 768
7	128	16	65 536
8	256	17	131 072

Next, look for the 1's in your binary number (ignoring all the 0's). Write down in another Table the Place Nos. of all these 1's and, in a separate column, their Decimal Equivalents. Then add up the latter column, and you have the Decimal Equivalent of your binary number.

Thus, in the Example given, the important Place Nos. are 0, 3, 5 and 10. (All the other Place Nos. lie over zero's in the binary number, and so don't count.) Construct the final Table thus:—

Place No.	Decimal Equivalent
0	1
3	8
5	32
10	1 024
	1 065

The advantages of using digital systems are as follows:—

1. The voltage difference between the 0 and 1 levels can be made large enough to ensure freedom from interference.

2. The maximum error in a system can be kept as low as $\pm$ half a digit.

3. Semiconductors used in digital circuits are either cut-off or bottomed, except during the very rapid changeover period. Power dissipation is therefore very low, and circuits can be made almost immune to variations in either temperature or component values.

4. The use of digital logic in machine control makes it easy to couple machines to computers.

5.Digital logic circuits are particularly easy to produce in IC form.

6. Conversion from digital to analogue ("D to A") or from analogue to digital ("A to D") is possible. Digital methods can therefore be used to replace analogue circuits in many applications.

Logic Gates

Logic gates are circuits having several inputs and one output. The voltage level, either 0 or 1, at the output depends only on the inputs which are present *at any given instant of time*. Logic gates are designed in such a way that any desired combination of inputs can be made to produce an output 1, but that *no other combination* of input signals can produce an output 1.

The desired action of any logic gate system is governed by its so-called **truth table** and **Boolean expression.** Given suitable circuitry, any combination is possible — say, a gate whose output is 1 only when the inputs are 1,0,1,0 (in which case it is called a *four-input gate*).

Rather than produce an integrated circuit gate for every possible application, manufacturers make standardised circuits which can be used just like other circuit components. Some important standard gates, together with their International and British Standard symbols and Truth Tables, are shown in Fig. 9.3.

Truth Tables and Boolean Algebra

The truth value for the output Q of an AND gate with two inputs A and B is written $Q = A.B$. This means that the output is only at Logic 1 when both A *and* B are Logic 1. Similarly the output for a two-input OR gate would be written $Q = A+B$, the output being Logic 1 when *either* A *or* B is Logic 1.

Note that the symbols . and + have been chosen to represent AND and OR respectively, because they behave in logic in a way similar to that in which multiplication and addition behave in normal arithmetic.

When an input/output relationship is stated as being the *inverse* of the other, as in the case of the NOT gate, this is written $Q = \bar{A}$ — with the bar over the letter A representing "NOT A".

The written expressions for NOT AND = NAND and NOT OR = NOR then become $Q = \overline{A.B}$ and $Q = \overline{A + B}$ respectively.

The two symbols labelled *"EX-OR"* and *"EX-NOR"* in Fig. 9.3 stand for *"Exclusive OR"* and *"Exclusive NOR"* respectively. It will be seen that the "Exclusive OR" function is similar to that of the OR gate except that it rules out the case where A = B = 1. The Boolean expression can be read from the truth table as $Q = \bar{A}.B + A.\bar{B}$

The "Exclusive NOR" function is obviously the negation of "Exclusive OR". Its output is *true* (*i.e.* at Logic 1) when both A and B have the same value. It is in fact

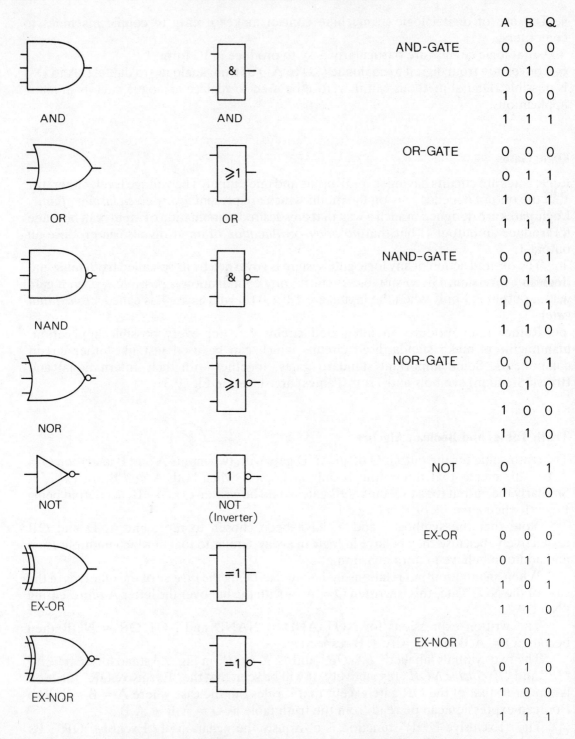

		A	B	Q
AND-GATE		0	0	0
		0	1	0
		1	0	0
		1	1	1
OR-GATE		0	0	0
		0	1	1
		1	0	1
		1	1	1
NAND-GATE		0	0	1
		0	1	1
		1	0	1
		1	1	0
NOR-GATE		0	0	1
		0	1	0
		1	0	0
		1	1	0
NOT		0		1
		1		0
EX-OR		0	0	0
		0	1	1
		1	0	1
		1	1	0
EX-NOR		0	0	1
		0	1	0
		1	0	0
		1	1	1

Fig. 9.3   **LOGIC SYMBOLS and TRUTH TABLES.**

sometimes called for this reason the *Coincidence Gate*. The Boolean expression for it is Q = $\bar{A}.\bar{B}$ + A.B

A relationship between the "Exclusive OR" and the "Exclusive NOR" functions can be developed, using the Boolean expressions and the NOT function as follows:

$$\bar{A}.B + A.\bar{B} = \bar{A}.\bar{B} + A.B$$

Many other more complex logic functions can be equated in a similar way by using truth tables or the rules of Boolean algebra.

The ICs Used in Digital Logic Circuits

At the time of writing, two "families" of IC circuits are used in digital circuits — the **TTL** (Transistor-Transistor-Logic) and the **CMOS** (Complementary-Metal-Oxide-Silicon).

TTL ICs (see Fig. 9.4) use bipolar transistors in integrated form, with their input or inputs always connected to the emitter of a transistor whose base is connected, through a resistor, to +5V. With this type of logic, an input which is kept at Logic 1 (+ 5V) consumes no current (apart from a small leakage current); but an input kept at Logic 0 (zero volts) will pass 1.6 mA, so that the connection between the gate input and zero volts must possess low resistance.

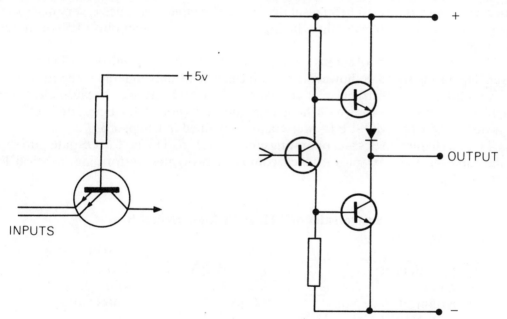

Fig. 9.4   The TTL (TRANSISTOR-TRANSISTOR-LOGIC) IC.

Each gate output can drive a current of, typically, 16 mA either to earth (*supplying current*) or from the +5V line (*sinking current*). Each gate output can therefore drive up to ten other gate inputs (AND, OR, NAND, NOR, NOT types). In the language of logic design, the gate has a *fan-out of ten*. The opposite term, *fan-in,* refers to the number of possible inputs to a gate which need to be driven.

Some care has to be taken if more than one output is used to drive an input. The usual gate output circuit is a totem-pole circuit, in which the output terminal can be shorted through one of the transistors either to earth or to +5V. It is important that gates using this type of output circuit (as most do) should never have their outputs connected together; for if one output were at 1 and the other at 0, destructively high currents would pass through both gates.

When gate outputs *must* be connected (in a type of circuit called the *wire-OR*), it is essential to use a gate with a "floating" output. Such a gate has an output stage containing only one transistor, with no load. A resistor load external to the circuit itself must therefore be provided. It is known as a *pull-up resistor*.

An important point to note about all TTL circuits is that any unconnected input, or any input which has a resistance of more than 100 ohms in series, will "float" to the base voltage of +5V because of emitter-follower action. At the high operating speeds normal for TTL gates, unconnected inputs can cause trouble through pickup of interference pulses. All unused inputs should therefore be connected to the +5V line through resistors of 1k or so.

For d.c. or low-speed operation, this precaution is less important.

In the *CMOS family of ICs*, field-effect transistors in their integrated form are used, with every input connected to an insulated gate. The input resistance is very high, so that input current is negligible whether the input signal is 1 or 0. Fan-outs of 50 or more are therefore possible.

A much wider range of supply voltages can be tolerated, though operating speeds are lower. Operating speed is, however, a significant factor only in large computers.

Careful circuit construction is necessary with CMOS devices because electrostatic voltages can cause breakdown of the gate of the FET (not of the logic gate itself) in the ways described when MOSFET's were being explained in Chapter 3.

Typical characteristics and operating conditions for TTL and CMOS gates are shown in the table on the next page, which compares two gates performing identical logic functions.

Characteristics of TTL and CMOS Digital ICs

General Data

	TTL	CMOS
Supply Voltage	4.75 to 5.25V	4 to 12V
Fan-out	About 10	More than 50
Operating Temperature	0°C to 70°C	−40°C to + 80°C
4-input NAND Gates		
Input Current	40µA to 1.6 mA	10 pA
Output Drive Current	30 mA	0.25 mA
Switching Time Delay	11 ns	300 ns

Most IC gates are multiple, for it is as easy to package four two-input gates as one. The most commonly-encountered packages are the *DIL (Dual-in-line)* 14- and 16-pin types whose pin-numbering schemes are shown in Fig. 9.5.

Fig 9.6 shows a DIL package in outline.

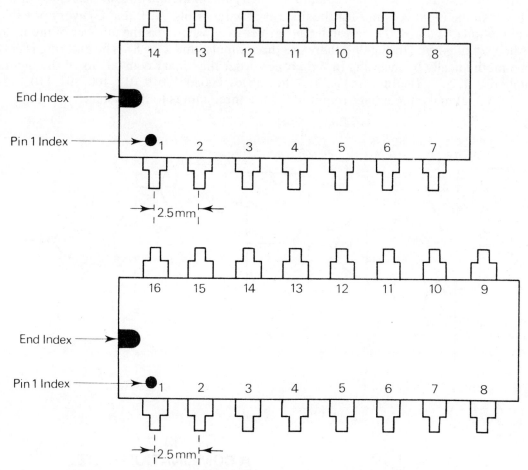

Fig. 9.5   DUAL-IN LINE IC Packages, 14-pin and 16-pin.

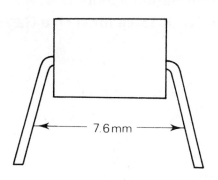

Fig 9.6
A DIL PACKAGE in Outline.

Gate Combinations

To establish the truth table for a combination of gates, such as that shown in Fig. 9.7 proceed as follows:—

1. Draw up a table, allowing one column for each gate input, and one for the final output.
2. Enter in the input columns for the first set of gates (Cols. A, B and C) every possible combination of 1 and 0. There will be $2n$ such entries, where n is the number of inputs to the first set of gates. (In Fig. 9.7 there are three inputs, and $2^3 = 8$). The entering is best done methodically by inserting in the proper order the binary equivalents of the digital numbers $0, 1, 2 \ldots$ (in this case) 7. Thus the entries: 000, 001, 010, 011, 100, 101, 110, 111, in Fig. 9.7 (c) make the 8 lines required for the three inputs to the system.

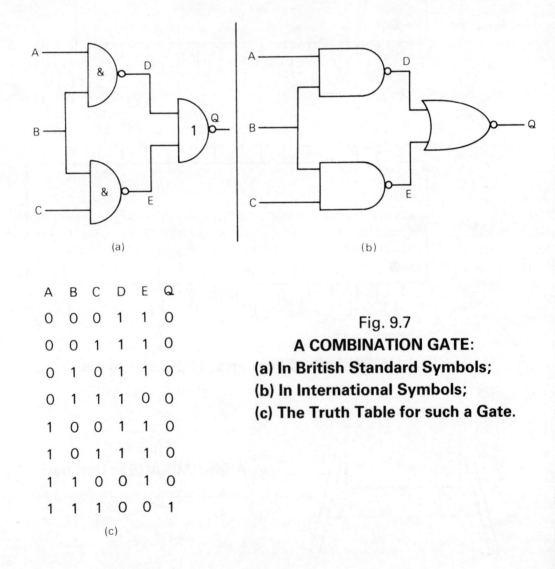

(a)

(b)

A	B	C	D	E	Q
0	0	0	1	1	0
0	0	1	1	1	0
0	1	0	1	1	0
0	1	1	1	0	0
1	0	0	1	1	0
1	0	1	1	1	0
1	1	0	0	1	0
1	1	1	0	0	1

(c)

Fig. 9.7

A COMBINATION GATE:

(a) In British Standard Symbols;

(b) In International Symbols;

(c) The Truth Table for such a Gate.

3. With the truth tables for every combination of gates known from Fig. 9.3 enter the outputs of the first set of gates in Cols. D and E respectively. These outputs now constitute the inputs for the next set of gates, which are entered in Col. Q.

4. Had there been more than eight inputs into the gate combination under analysis, the same procedure would have been followed until the table was complete and the final output signal determined.

Example. Find the truth table for the circuit of Fig. 9.7.

Solution. Note first that Figs. 9.7 (a) and (b) depict the same circuit, (a) showing it in British Standard notation and (b) in the International Notation. The circuit consists of two NAND gates followed by an OR gate. Turn to Fig. 9.3 for the truth table relevant to a two-input logic gate so constructed.

Then draw up a blank truth table, labelling the system inputs A, B and C. Label the intermediate inputs D and E, and the output Q. Enter in the table all the possible values of inputs, using the ordinary binary sequence 000, 001, 010, 011, 100, etc. This should automatically give the correct number of lines in the table.

Now enter Column D from the truth table for the NAND gate, which is always 1 except when both inputs are 1. Fill in Col. E with the output of the other NAND gate.

With Cols. D and E complete, Col. Q can also be completed — using this time the truth table for the NOR gate, an output which is 0 if *either* D or E is 1. The final truth table will look as illustrated in Fig. 9.7 (c).

Exercise 9.1

For this and other exercises using TTL circuits, a suitable "breadboard" for mounting and connecting TTL IC's is needed. The "Euro-Breadboard" mentioned in Chapter 4 is well suited to the job. IC's are plugged into the spaces provided, and other connections made by plugging components or wires into the holes on the board.

Connect a 7400 IC into place, using the circuits shown in Fig. 9.8 (a and b). The numbers shown on the diagram correspond to the pin numbers of the 14-pin IC package.

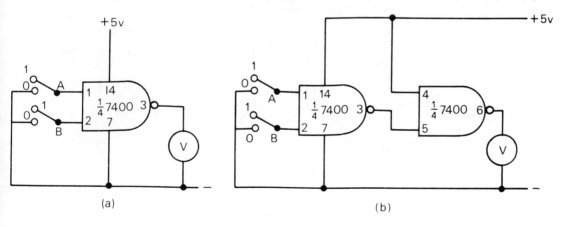

Fig. 9.8

Using the input switches, and a voltmeter to give the output voltages, draw up the two truth tables. Note that unless an input is connected to zero, its value is 1.

A 5V supply must be used. Higher voltages can damage the IC's, while the use of lower voltages will cause uncertain action.

R-S Flip-Flops

A flip-flop is a circuit of the bistable family. IC flip-flops tend to be of complex designs which would be uneconomical to manufacture with discrete components.

Fig. 9.9 shows a very simple flip-flop circuit, the so-called R-S flip-flop which can be formed (among other ways) by using two NAND gates connected as shown. (R-S flip-flops are also, of course, available as IC's in their own right).

The R-S flip-flop has two signal inputs, labelled respectively R and S, and two outputs, labelled Q and $\bar{Q}$. A bar drawn above a letter in this way denotes an *inverse*, so that if Q = 1, then $\bar{Q}$ = 0; if Q = 0, then $\bar{Q}$ = 1. The truth table for this circuit demonstrates an important point distinguishing this and all other flip-flop circuits from simple gate circuits. Flip-flops belong to a class of circuits called *sequential logic circuits* in which the output Q has a value which depends on the *previous* value of the inputs as well as on their present value. The output of a logic gate, by contrast, depends only on the values of inputs which are present *at the same time* as the output. Thus in Fig. 9.9 the truth table output for the inputs R = 1 and S = 1 depends on what values of R and S existed immediately before the R = 1, S = 1 state. If the previous state was R=0, S=1, then the arrival of R=1, S=1 gives Q=1. If the previous state was R=1, S=0, then the arrival of R=1, S=1 gives Q=0.

Note that there is no line R=0, S=0 for the R-S flip-flop. Such an input would give

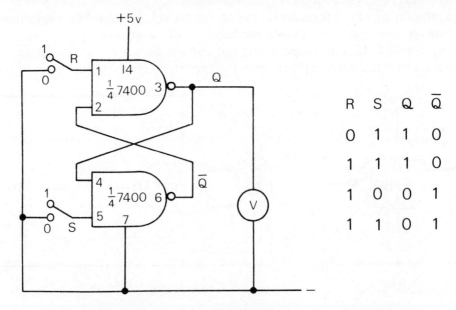

R	S	Q	$\bar{Q}$
0	1	1	0
1	1	1	0
1	0	0	1
1	1	0	1

Fig. 9.9   The R-S FLIP-FLOP and its Truth Table.

$Q=1, \bar{Q} = 1$, which is not permissible. Moreover, R-S flip-flops can only be used when the state R=0, S=0 cannot possibly arise. For this reason other types of flip-flops, such as the D-type and the J-K type, are used in most logic applications.

Exercise 9.2
Connect two gates of a 7400 in the form of an R-S flip-flop, as in Fig. 9.9. Use voltmeters to indicate the states of Q and $\bar{Q}$, and switches to provide the inputs. Draw up the truth table.

Clocked Flip-Flops

The simple R-S flip-flop changes state when either input becomes, or is set to, zero. Most digital circuits require flip-flops which change state only when told to do so by means of a pulse, called a *clock-pulse,* arriving at a separate input. In such *clocked flip-flops,* all the flip-flops in a circuit can be made to change state at the same time.

Clocking has the advantage that the inputs need only be set an instant before the arrival of the clock pulse — changes of state at the inputs at any other time having no effect on the output. Between clock pulses, the output remains as it was when set by the last clock pulse.

D-Type Flip-Flops

The so-called *D-type flip-flop* shown in Fig. 9.10 (a) triggers on the leading edge of the clock pulse. The logic value on the D input is then transferred to the Q output, thus delaying the data by the period of one clock pulse.

Reference to the truth table in Fig. 9.10 (b) shows the action of the **Preset (Pr)** and **Clear (Clr)** inputs. They are used to set the initial output states of the device. When Pr=0, Q is set to 1. When Clr=0, Q is set to 0. The states of both *Clk* and *D* are irrelevant at this moment of time because *Pr* and *Clr* override them. Only when *Pr=Clr=1* will the clock pulse transfer the data, and even then only as the clock pulse reaches a high value.

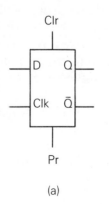

Pr	Clr	Clk	D	Q	$\bar{Q}$
0	1	×	×	1	0
1	0	×	×	0	1
0	0	×	×	1	1
1	1	↑	1	1	0
1	1	↑	0	0	1
1	1	0	×	Q	$\bar{Q}$

(a)   (b)

Fig. 9.10   **The D-Type Flip-Flop.**

The state where *Pr=Clr=0* represents an unstable condition in a D-type flip-flop, and is prohibited.

J-K Flip-Flops

The most common type of clocked flip-flop is the J-K type represented by the symbol shown in Fig. 9.11. This type of flip-flop has three signal inputs labelled "set" and "reset" (or sometimes "pre-set" and "clear") which work independently of the clock pulses, and the usual two outputs Q and $\bar{Q}$ (with $\bar{Q}$ always the inverse of Q for any combination of inputs).

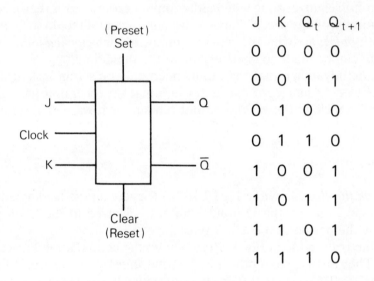

J	K	Q_t	Q_{t+1}
0	0	0	0
0	0	1	1
0	1	0	0
0	1	1	0
1	0	0	1
1	0	1	1
1	1	0	1
1	1	1	0

Fig. 9.11   The J-K FLIP-FLOP: Symbol and Truth Table.

A full discussion of the uses of the J-K flip-flop is outside the scope of this book, so the following outline will be brief. The J and K inputs control the voltage levels to which the output will change when the *trailing* edge of the clock pulse arrives. When the *leading* edge of the clock pulse arrives, the two inputs are used to pre-set what the output will eventually be, but the change-over itself only takes place when the trailing edge of the clock pulse arrives.

The truth table for the J-K flip-flop is also shown in Fig. 9.11, in which Q_t stands for the output voltage at Q before the clock pulse arrives and Q_{t+1} for the output at the Q terminal after the clock pulse has passed. The "Set/Reset" inputs are used to change the value of Q at any time before, during or after the arrival of the clock pulse. Connecting the "Set" terminal to zero volts causes the output at Q to go to Logic 1; connecting the "Reset" terminal to zero volts causes the output at Q to go to Logic 0.

The familiar bistable counting action described in Chapter 7 occurs when both J and

K inputs are taken to + 5V (in the case of TTL circuits). Two clock pulses arriving at the clock terminal give rise to one pulse at the Q output, while a pulse of inverse polarity will simultaneously reach the $\bar{Q}$ output.

Exercise 9.3
Connect the circuit shown in Fig. 9.12 using a TTL 7476 IC, which contains two J-K flip-flops, and (preferably) a Euro-Breadboard. Apply clock pulses either from a slow pulse generator or from a "debounced switch" (see below), and observe the output indicator LED's.

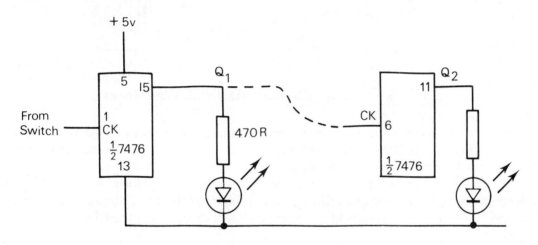

Fig. 9.12

Now connect the clock terminal (pin 6 of the second flip-flop in the package) to the Q-output (pin 15 of the first flip-flop), and re-apply the slow clock pulses. Observe the indicators.

Remember that all unconnected pins of TTL IC's will "float" to +5V, so that no connections need be made to any pin which is to be kept at Logic 1 when such slow clock pulses are applied. When CMOS logic systems are used, no pin must ever be left disconnected.

Switch De-Bouncing

When the output of a mechanical switch — either hand-operated or forming part of a thermostat, pressure switch, etc. — is used to feed pulses to a digital circuit, some precautions have to be taken to prevent "bounce".

When two mechanical contacts make, the elasticity of the metals involved generally gives rise to one or more tiny bounces, each lasting a millisecond or so, before the switch contacts finally close. The waveform derived from such a switch closure is shown in Fig. 9.13. If fed into the clock input of a counter, for example, it would cause serious miscounting, since each bounce would be counted as a switch operation. Circuits in which a mechanical switch is used to feed a counter must therefore have some means of eliminating the unwanted pulses caused by contact bounce.

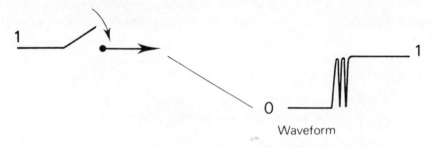

Waveform

Fig. 9.13   The SWITCH-BOUNCE Waveform.

Fig. 9.14 shows two forms of de-bouncing circuit. The circuit of 9.14(a) contains a two-way switch and an R-S flip-flop, and takes advantage of the fact that the output of the R-S flip-flop does not change when one of its inputs is taken to Logic 1.

The circuit of Fig. 9.14(b) employs a Schmitt trigger, in the form of a TTL IC gate with Schmitt characteristics, and an integrator at the input. If the switch contacts bounce, the capacitor cannot charge quickly enough to change the state of the trigger.

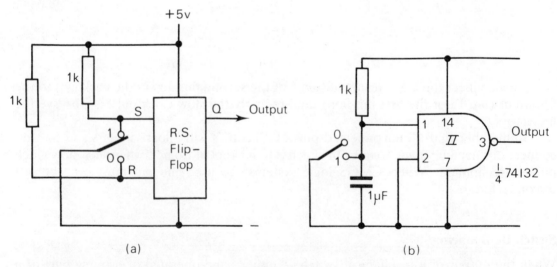

(a)   (b)

Fig. 9.14
"DE-BOUNCING" CIRCUITS: (a) With R-S flip-flop (b) With Schmitt Trigger.

Note, by the way, that clock pulse inputs to digital circuits must have short rise and fall times. The inputs to gates also should never be slow-changing waveforms. The reason is that the gain of these circuits, considered as amplifiers, is very large, so that a slow-changing waveform at the input can momentarily bias the circuit in a linear mode, so making oscillation possible. Oscillation also can cause mis-counting and erratic operation.

Counting and Decoding

A fundamental feature of all bistable devices is that they divide the input by two. Thus for every *two* clock-pulse inputs, the Q output changes *once*. This concept forms the basis of electronic binary counters, an example of which is shown in Fig. 9.15.

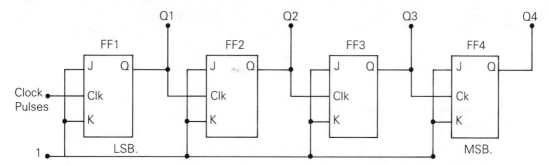

Fig. 9.15   **The RIPPLE or ASYNCHRONOUS COUNTER.**

The pulse sequence to be counted is the input to FF1, whose Q output now provides the clock for the next stage, and so on. A count input to the first stage thus "ripples" through the circuit — which is why a counter of this type is often called a *ripple*, a *ripple-through* or an *asynchronous* counter. Note that the output count should be read from right to left, because the *Most Significant Bit (MSB)* is on the right.

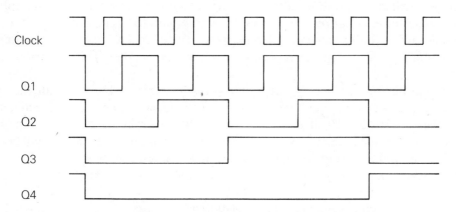

Fig. 9.16   **BINARY COUNTER WAVEFORMS.**

The ripple counter's waveforms are shown in Fig. 9.16. Since J=K=1, the Q output *toggles*, or changes, on the edge of every negative-going waveform.

When the Q̄ output of every stage of a flip-flop is used to provide the clock pulses, the circuit *counts down* from a preset number, to produce a *ripple-down* counter.

If the control circuit shown in Fig. 9.17 is added between each flip-flop, it is possible to produce a counter which will count up or down according to the state of the control line. If control is Logic 1, the circuit will count up; while if the control is Logic 0, it will count down.

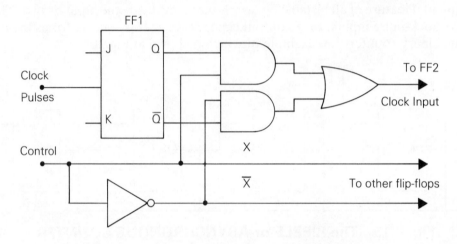

Fig. 9.17   **The UP-DOWN COUNTER CONTROL.**

Ripple counters are used when only a few stages of counting are needed. High-speed multi-stage counters call for the use of synchronous counters, in which the same clock pulse is taken to every flip-flop. Their action is beyond the scope of this book.

As assembly of flip-flops in the form of a binary counter, whether ripple or synchronous, will give an output taking the form of a binary number. In most applications involving the display of figures, a conversion from binary to decimal will be needed. This operation is carried out by a *decoder*. Conversely, if a decimal number is to be entered into a binary counter, a decimal-to-binary conversion will be needed. This is carried out by an *encoder*.

A simple decimal-to-binary encoder is shown in Fig. 9.18. With all the switches corresponding to decimal numbers open, all four output lines are connected to +5V through resistors R_1, R_2, R_3 or R_4. This has the effect of making all the outputs Logic 1. When a decimal switch is closed, however, one or more of the vertical lines will be earthed as the relevant diodes start to conduct. These earthed lines at once switch to Logic 0, with all the unearthed lines remaining at Logic 1. The binary numbers can thus be read from the outputs. (Note, once more, how the values of binary numbers *rise from right to left*, from 2^0 (which is 1) through 2^1 (which is 2) to 2 to the power of two, 2^3, 2^4 — and so on for as far as one cares to go).

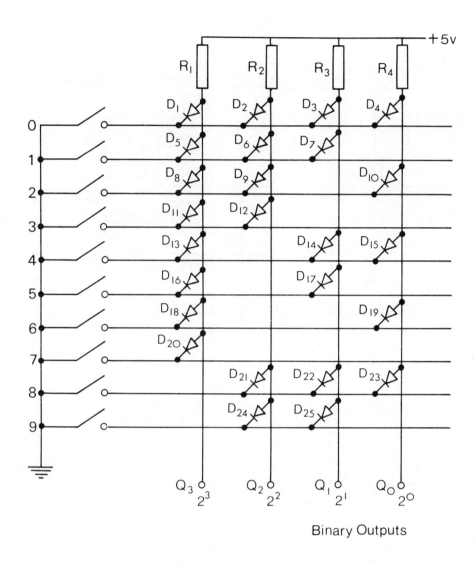

Binary Outputs

Fig. 9.18 **A DECIMAL-TO-BINARY ENCODER.**

The reverse operation, binary-to-decimal decoding, is less simple in terms of components needed — both inverters and gates being required, as shown in Fig. 9.19. It will be good practice for the reader to study this circuit critically, working out the different voltage levels which will be present for every possible binary input. Remember that every binary input will cause its corresponding decimal output to go to Logic 1. There must never be an output for the binary numbers corresponding to decimal figures 10, 11, 12, 13, 14, 15 . . . etc.

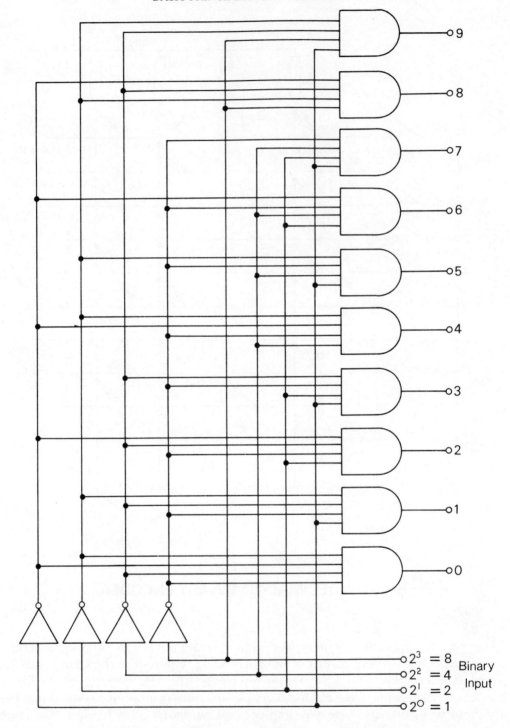

Fig. 9.19   **A BINARY-TO-DECIMAL DECODER.**

Displays

A binary number can be displayed (though they seldom are) by using filament lamps or LED indicators connected to the Q output of each bistable. Decimal displays, however, are much more useful, and the decoder system outlined above nearly always requires a decimal display to make its results visible.

Among the types of decimal display commonly used are incandescent (filament) lamps, cold-cathode displays, and LED and liquid crystal displays (LCD's). The techniques necessary to obtain a display differ somewhat from one type of display to another.

Incandescent or filament displays are commonly used to give very large displays — needed in some industrial applications and consisting of a set of lamps which illuminate slides on which decimal numbers are outlined. An optical projection system then displays the selected figure on a screen. Since each lamp displays one figure only, a binary-to-decimal decoder of the type shown in Fig. 9.19 will be suitable, though a driver stage will generally be needed to supply the power needed by the lamps. Such a driver stage is often referred to as an *interface* — a general term used for any circuit needed to couple digital logic either to other circuits or to digital circuits operating at different voltage levels.

Cold-cathode displays rely on the fact that a gas at low pressure will conduct at a voltage between 45V and 210V, depending on the composition and pressure of the gas. When the gas conducts, a bright glow surrounds the cathode (negative) electrode which is

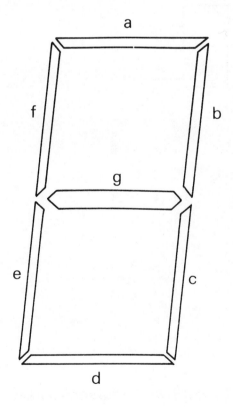

Fig. 9.20

The Structure of a

SEVEN-SEGMENT DISPLAY.

in contact with the gas. If this cathode is made in the shape of a figure or a letter, the glow too will take this shape when the gas conducts. A cold-cathode display therefore comprises an anode (a nickel wire) and ten cathodes shaped in the form of the figures 0 to 9, all enclosed in a glass bulb containing a gas — usually neon — at low pressure. When a suitable voltage exists between the anode and one of the cathodes, a glow will appear around that cathode, so illuminating its figure.

Because of the high voltage levels involved, an interface circuit is also needed. For decoding, the binary-decimal decoder of Fig. 9.19 is suitable.

LED displays make use of the glow which occurs when current passes through a diode made of gallium arsenide, or of similar materials such as indium phosphide. LCD displays make use of the fact that some materials become opaque when an electric field, caused by a voltage, is applied across them between conducting plates.

In either type of display, the materials are formed into the seven-segment shape shown in Fig. 9.20 — the segments identified by letters as shown. From this basic shape, a complete set of figures (plus a few letters) can be constructed by selecting suitable segments for illumination.

A binary-to-decimal decoder is unsuitable for this type of display, which requires a new kind of truth table for a binary-decimal seven-segment decoder. Such a truth table is shown in Fig. 9.21.

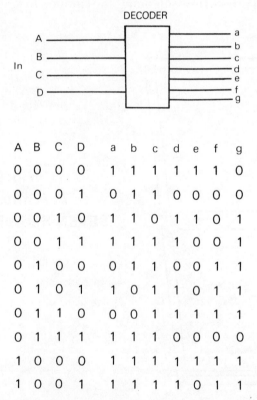

A	B	C	D	a	b	c	d	e	f	g
0	0	0	0	1	1	1	1	1	1	0
0	0	0	1	0	1	1	0	0	0	0
0	0	1	0	1	1	0	1	1	0	1
0	0	1	1	1	1	1	1	0	0	1
0	1	0	0	0	1	1	0	0	1	1
0	1	0	1	1	0	1	1	0	1	1
0	1	1	0	0	0	1	1	1	1	1
0	1	1	1	1	1	1	0	0	0	0
1	0	0	0	1	1	1	1	1	1	1
1	0	0	1	1	1	1	1	0	1	1

Fig. 9.21 **Truth Table for a Binary Seven-Segment Decoder.**

Both LED and LCD displays require lower voltages than cold-cathode displays; and LED displays are manufactured in two types, either as common anodes or as common cathodes. A common anode display needs a Logic 0 connection to a cathode to illuminate a bar; a common cathode needs a Logic 1 connected to an anode to illuminate a bar. LED displays are more visible in poor conditions of light, and are fully compatible with logic systems since they require low voltage d.c. for their operation.

LCD displays require some form of interface because an a.c. voltage of 10V to 30V, peak-to-peak, is needed at a frequency between 30 Hz and 200 Hz. Decoder-driver IC's are available for each type of display.

Strobing

Many displays are *strobed,* which means that only one display at a time is switched on in a multi-digit display. This technique can be used to reduce the number of active circuits — though at the expense of added complexity (of circuit diagram, be it said, rather than of actual connections).

In a strobed display, one decoder driver is connected to all of the displays; and the counters are connected to the decoder-driver by a circuit called a *multiplexer,* which is a switch circuit operated by a coded input. A clock pulse, called in this operation a *strobe pulse,* is used to switch the multiplexer, and also to brighten up each display. The first figure from the counter is decoded and displayed on its segments; then the next strobe pulse switches the inputs of the decoder to the next stage of the counter — and the bright-up pulse to the next set of segments — so that the next figure is shown.

The strobing is carried out at very high speed, so that what the observer sees appears to be a continuous set of figures, rather than figures illuminated in very rapid sequence. Strobing circuits are often included as part of a large IC (such as the clock IC's used for digital clocks), so that only the connections to the display require to be made.

Logic Probes

The testing of logic circuits is made considerably easier by the use of logic probes. A logic probe will indicate the state of the logic voltage, 0 or 1, at every pin of an IC. By clipping the probe over an IC, therefore, every input and output voltage can be read simultaneously.

For logic probes to be used effectively, all clock pulses must be stopped. Alternatively, resort must be had to slow clocking techniques while fault-finding is in progress.

More advanced types of logic probe, however, can distinguish between steady voltages and voltages consisting of pulses rapidly succeeding one another. They can therefore be used to test circuits to which normal clock signals are being applied.

INDEX